D1278184

Grammar, Usage, & Mechanics

Skillbook

Level G

Perfection Learning®

© **2007 by Perfection Learning**®

Please visit our Web site at:
www.perfectionlearning.com

When ordering this book, please specify:
Softcover: ISBN 978-0-7891-7052-1 or **74567S**
Reinforced Library Binding: ISBN 978-1-61563-014-1or **7456702**

12 13 14 15 16 PP 23 22 21 20 19

Printed in the United States of America

Table of Contents

Chapter 1: The Parts of a Sentence

Chapter 2: Nouns and Pronouns

Chapter 3: Verbs

Chapter 4: Adjectives and Adverbs

Table of Contents

Table of Contents

Chapter 16: End Marks and Commas

Chapter 17: Italics and Quotation Marks

Chapter 18: Other Punctuation

Table of Contents

CHAPTER 1   The Parts of a Sentence   *(pages 2–9)*

Combining Subjects and Predicates

A **sentence** is a group of words that expresses a complete thought.

◆ Combine a subject from Column A with a predicate in Column B to form a
sentence that makes sense. Begin each sentence with a capital letter and end
each one with a period.

A	B
orange juice	cooks breakfast every day
the eggs	looks delicious
my mom	belongs to my brother
many good mornings	is my favorite meal
breakfast at our house	starts with a glass of milk
the food on the table	cook in the pan
the task of cleaning up	provides calcium
bacon	begin with breakfast
a glass of milk	sizzles on the stove
breakfast	contains vitamin C

1. _____

2. _____

3. _____

4. _____

5. _____

6. _____

7. _____

8. _____

9. _____

10. _____

CHAPTER 1   The Parts of a Sentence   *(pages 2–9)*

Completing Sentences

◆ Complete each of the sentence fragments below by adding either a subject or a predicate.

◆ Every morning my mother

1. _____

_____

◆ A bowl of cereal

2. _____

_____

◆ wants us to eat a good breakfast

3. _____

_____

◆ spilled all over the new carpet

4. _____

_____

CHAPTER 1 **The Parts of a Sentence** *(pages 2–9)*

Finding Complete Subjects

A **complete subject** includes all the words used to identify the person, place, thing, or idea that the sentence is about.

◆ Underline each complete subject.

1. Schools of fish stay together for protection.

2. An average goldfish lives four years.

3. The horseshoe crab existed in its current form 500 million years ago.

4. A small trout swims faster than a person.

5. The upside-down catfish floats on its back.

6. The huge whale shark eats only small plants and small water animals, not people.

7. The world's smallest frog fits inside a thimble.

8. The common sponge is a sea animal with a soft skeleton.

9. The basket starfish has more than 80,000 arms up to fifteen inches long.

10. Scientists around the world have identified about 21,000 different kinds of fish.

CHAPTER 1   **The Parts of a Sentence**   *(pages 2–9)*

Finding Complete and Simple Subjects

A **simple subject** is the main word in the complete subject.

◆ Underline each complete subject <u>once</u>. Then underline each simple subject <u><u>twice</u></u>.

1. A heavy shower ended the month-long drought.

2. The cotton in the fields needed the rain.

3. Texas receives little rainfall in July.

4. With huge grins the local farmers welcomed the heavy rain.

5. Doppler radar tracked the active storm system across the county.

6. The large trees next door survived the storm.

7. My younger brother danced joyfully in the rain.

8. Many people enjoyed the summer storm.

9. Corn in the fields began to ripen.

10. The TV meteorologist predicted the arrival of the violent storm.

CHAPTER 1   The Parts of a Sentence   *(pages 2–9)*

Finding Complete and Simple Subjects

◆ Underline each complete subject <u>once</u>. Then underline each simple subject <u><u>twice</u></u>.

1. China is the third-largest country in the world.

2. *Viking I* took pictures of the surface of Mars.

3. A healthy person can take twelve to eighteen breaths per minute.

4. Hair on your head grows about $\frac{1}{100}$ of an inch daily.

5. Robert Fulton built the first successful steamboat.

6. The Statue of Liberty is almost 152 feet high.

7. Chinese inventors of the 12th century created the compass.

8. The first transatlantic journey in a hot-air balloon was in 1978.

9. Ancient Egyptians were the first to develop a calendar year that included 365 days.

10. Elephants reach old age at about sixty-five.

CHAPTER 1   **The Parts of a Sentence**   *(pages 2–9)*

Using Complete or Simple Subjects

◆ Follow the directions to write complete sentences.

◆ Use the word *boys* as a simple subject.

1. _____

_____

◆ Use the word *teacher* as part of a complete subject.

2. _____

_____

◆ Use the word *cat* as part of a complete subject.

3. _____

_____

◆ Use the word *students* as a simple subject.

4. _____

_____

◆ Use any two-word noun as a simple subject.

5. _____

_____

CHAPTER 1 **The Parts of a Sentence** *(pages 2–9)*

Finding Complete Predicates

A **complete predicate** includes all the words that tell what the subject is doing or that tell something about the subject.

◆ <u>Underline</u> each complete predicate.

1. That zany zebra plays the zither.

2. A big bear with a balloon bolted through the barn.

3. Furry foxes fought fiercely for food.

4. The giant giraffes greeted me graciously.

5. Lazy llamas from Liberia licked the lemons.

6. Chilly chipmunks chattered cheerfully.

7. The brown baboons banged on the bongo drums.

8. The round raccoons raced the reindeer.

9. The timid tiger tripped on a torn tuxedo.

10. Pudgy pandas played the piano with precision.

11. Giant gorillas gathered guavas for guests.

12. Kangaroos kept kiwis in their kitchens.

13. Worms wrestled with weary wasps in watermelons.

14. Capable cheetahs challenged customers to chess.

15. Slippery seals sounded the shiny saxophones.

CHAPTER 1   The Parts of a Sentence   *(pages 2–9)*

Finding Complete Predicates and Verbs

A **simple predicate**, or **verb**, is the main word or phrase in the complete predicate.

◆ Underline each complete predicate <u>once</u>. Then underline each verb <u>twice</u>.

1. The largest state in the United States is Alaska.

2. The Alaskan pipeline transports crude oil over land.

3. The Underground is the name of London's busy subway system.

4. Christopher Columbus's discoveries in 1492 led to the European settlement of the Americas.

5. The Pyrenees Mountains separate France from Spain.

6. Lafayette sailed from France to America on March 26, 1777.

7. The Black Sea is along the northern coast of Turkey and below the southern coast of Ukraine.

8. The Mississippi River divides the eastern United States from the western United States.

9. The Rio Grande borders Mexico and Texas.

10. California's coastline runs along the Pacific Ocean.

CHAPTER 1   The Parts of a Sentence   *(pages 2–9)*

Finding Verbs

◆ <u>Underline</u> each verb.

1. The infielder caught the ball for an out.

2. Their brothers are the umpires for tonight's game.

3. Paul worries about his batting average.

4. I thought about your suggestion for a new coach.

5. Dad was a coach for my team last year.

6. The pitcher threw the ball quickly to second base.

7. Jerry played on Sue's team.

8. Kyle dreamed of home runs.

9. The coach yelled at the players.

10. The most popular team sport in our small town is baseball.

Name _____ Date _____

Expanding Sentences

◆ Revise the following sentences, which do not contain enough information, by adding information to the simple predicate.

◆ The catcher missed.

1. _____

_____

◆ John hit.

2. _____

_____

◆ Myra batted.

3. _____

_____

◆ The shortstop tagged.

4. _____

_____

◆ I play.

5. _____

_____

◆ Samantha pitched.

6. _____

_____

CHAPTER 1 — **The Parts of a Sentence** *(pages 2–9)*

Finding Verb Phrases

The main verb and any helping verbs make up a **verb phrase**.

◆ <u>Underline</u> each verb phrase.

1. Drew might audition for a part in the school play.

2. Sarah may be singing in the talent show tomorrow.

3. Karen can memorize almost anything.

4. Next month I will volunteer as a set painter.

5. The drama club does practice an hour every afternoon after school.

6. The director should have warned us about the trap door on the set.

7. By the end of Saturday's rehearsal, the cast had blocked the entire first act of the play.

8. Susan did get the lead in the play.

9. My brother has forgotten his lines in the second act again this afternoon.

10. My family has invited the cast to a party after the performance.

CHAPTER 1   The Parts of a Sentence   *(pages 2–9)*

Finding Verb Phrases

◆ <u>Underline</u> each verb phrase.

1. We couldn't find the tent.

2. Will your brother drive us to the campground in Sumter County?

3. Does the campfire begin at sunset?

4. My sister can easily cook over an open fire.

5. Campers will often toast marshmallows.

6. Does Gina like camp life?

7. I have never been to this campground before.

8. Sabrina wouldn't help with the extra gear.

9. Would you swim in this lake?

10. Tom could easily bring his canoe along with us.

11. The boys can't forget their warm jackets.

12. Did you pack the lantern?

13. Molly has only brought enough food for dinner tonight and breakfast tomorrow.

14. What will she eat for breakfast?

15. Our parents are not going to the grocery store.

Name _____ Date _____

Writing Sentences Using Helping Verbs

Write a sentence for each verb. Include the helping verb *has* or *have* in at least two of your sentences. Then underline each subject <u>once</u> and each verb <u>twice</u>.

◆ paddled

1. _____

_____

◆ waded

2. _____

_____

◆ tumbled

3. _____

_____

◆ sunk

4. _____

_____

◆ raced

5. _____

_____

◆ sailed

6. _____

_____

CHAPTER 1 The Parts of a Sentence *(pages 2–9)*

Mixed Practice: Subjects and Verbs

◆ Underline the subject <u>once</u> and verb <u>twice</u> in each sentence.

1. Without William Webb Ellis, people wouldn't enjoy football today.

2. This little-known athlete of long ago scored football's first touchdown.

3. In 1823, Ellis was eagerly playing a game of soccer at Rugby School in England.

4. Soccer players could move the ball only with their feet and their heads.

5. Team members couldn't touch the ball with their hands in that game.

6. All of a sudden, Ellis grabbed the ball.

7. Ellis ran toward the goal line at the opposite end of the field.

8. The strange new play gave the game many more exciting possibilities.

9. A new game had just begun.

10. American football definitely was on its way.

11. Several teams organized the first American professional team in 1895.

12. In the early days of football, players didn't wear any equipment, not even helmets.

13. In the last seventy-five years, many changes have occurred in football.

14. For example, coaches developed the forward pass in 1906.

15. Now football captures the attention of millions of spectators.

CHAPTER 1 The Parts of a Sentence *(pages 2–9)*

Finding Subjects and Verbs

◆ Underline the subject <u>once</u> and verb <u>twice</u> in each sentence.

1. Is the faculty rehearsing the skits with the seventh graders for the comedy hour tonight?

2. There are not many tickets available anymore.

3. From the auditorium came a boisterous cheer during rehearsal today.

4. Did Allison finish her work on the set?

5. There are three door prizes for the students.

6. Can the teachers actually be funny?

7. Here is Ms. Barton in the center of the stage.

8. With a timid grin, she greeted the rowdy audience.

9. Over the P.A. system came the music for her song, "Yankee Doodle Dandy."

10. Through the auditorium ran Mr. Helms.

CHAPTER 1 **The Parts of a Sentence** *(pages 2–9)*

Finding Subjects and Verbs

◆ In each sentence, underline the subject <u>once</u> and the verb <u>twice</u>. If the subject is an understood you, insert *you* with an insert mark (^) where it belongs and <u>underline</u> it.

1. Did Nathan see a snowflake under his microscope during lab period today?

2. Write an entry in your journal every day this week about your science experiments.

3. During third period today, Mr. Brown will invite a guest speaker to our science class.

4. Along the edge of the glass beaker were dozens of tiny crystals.

5. Deliver my journal of experiments to Mr. Brown.

6. Read to the class your journal entry about our experiment with the hamster.

7. At the end of the class period, I will ask Mr. Brown about sound waves.

8. Is Dennis taking life science again this year?

9. Answer the question quickly.

10. Will salt dissolve in our solution?

CHAPTER 1   **The Parts of a Sentence**   *(pages 2–9)*

Using Different Positions of Subjects

◆ Rewrite any five of the sentences from the preceding exercise so that each
begins with the subject and is followed by the verb.

1. _____

_____

_____

2. _____

_____

_____

3. _____

_____

_____

4. _____

_____

_____

5. _____

_____

_____

CHAPTER 1 The Parts of a Sentence *(pages 2–9)*

Mixed Practice: Subjects and Verbs

◆ In each sentence, underline the subject <u>once</u> and the verb <u>twice</u>. If the subject is an understood you, insert *you* with an insert mark (^) where it belongs and <u>underline</u> it.

1. Do you know the poems of Edgar Allan Poe?

2. Have you ever read any of his short stories?

3. You can discover more about his personality.

4. There are many fans of his detective stories.

5. Didn't the Allans adopt him at the age of three?

6. Into schoolwork plunged young Poe.

7. At the beginning of his writing career were hundreds of publishing opportunities for his poetry.

8. Write an essay about "The Raven."

9. After the poems came fiction.

10. Did you ever read "The Masque of the Red Death"?

11. Here are some of his first detective stories.

12. To many literary publications, Poe contributed articles.

13. On your paper, write a description of C. Auguste Dupin, the main character in Poe's detective stories.

14. Poe worked as an editor throughout his life.

CHAPTER 1 **The Parts of a Sentence** *(pages 2–9)*

Finding Compound Subjects

A **compound subject** is two or more subjects in one sentence that have the same verb and are joined by a conjunction.

◆ Underline each compound subject. Remember that *and* and *or* are not considered part of the subject.

1. At the circus, clowns and acrobats will be featured.

2. Lions and elephants do not often appear in the same act.

3. Dancers and jugglers were photographed during the parade to the center ring.

4. Popcorn and cotton candy taste good at the circus.

5. Did horses, dogs, or lions perform in the show?

6. Only dedicated performers and gifted artists work for the circus.

7. A trapeze performance and a clown act are scheduled.

8. The ringmaster and the bandleader have arrived.

9. A tiger and a lion will perform tricks.

10. At today's circus were clowns, lions, and horses.

11. The dogs and the silly seals barked to the audience.

12. A magician and a bunny entertained the crowd.

13. A clown on stilts and a clown on a unicycle crashed.

14. Motorcycles and baby carriages were clown vehicles.

15. The elephants and the horses performed in different rings.

CHAPTER 1   The Parts of a Sentence   *(pages 2–9)*

Finding Compound Verbs

A **compound verb** is two or more verbs that have the same subject and are joined by a conjunction.

◆ Underline each compound verb. Remember that *and* and *or* are not considered part of the verb.

1. Janet has packed a lunch and will spend the day at the beach.

2. She will take pictures and develop them quickly.

3. Guy played in the sand and built a sand castle.

4. Mark walked the beach and looked for shells.

5. Brian fished for bait and caught a turtle.

6. Jean will run and swim at the beach.

7. Shirley caught the beach ball and threw it back.

8. Mark will take the boat to the repair shop or will fix it himself.

9. Cherri took a soda from the ice chest and drank it.

10. Mia applied sunscreen and removed her sunglasses.

CHAPTER 1 **The Parts of a Sentence** *(pages 2–9)*

Using Compound Subjects and Verbs

◆ Choose five sentences from the two previous exercises, and write them so that they include both a compound subject and a compound verb.

1. _____

_____

_____

2. _____

_____

_____

3. _____

_____

_____

4. _____

_____

_____

5. _____

_____

_____

CHAPTER 1   The Parts of a Sentence   *(pages 2–9)*

Mixed Practice: Subjects and Verbs

◆ Underline the subject once and verb twice in each sentence.

1. In 1951, a powerful hurricane and heavy winds were heading for Bermuda.

2. Weather forecasters and the people of the island were waiting for
   the hurricane with fear.

3. By noon the storm had almost reached the coast.

4. Trees and poles were swaying in the fierce wind.

5. Then a weather forecaster stopped and noticed something very strange.

6. A second hurricane was also traveling and blowing toward the island.

7. Eventually the second storm reached the first storm and smashed into it.

8. The collision weakened both hurricanes and threw them off course!

9. The storms changed course and headed toward the ocean.

10. The buildings and the people of the island survived both hurricanes.

11. The natives and tourists on the island were very happy and grateful.

12. The winds and water from the storm had caused much fear.

13. Water flooded buildings and eroded the beach.

14. Scientists and weather observers seldom have witnessed anything like
    those two hurricanes.

15. Wind and rain can cause a great deal of damage.

CHAPTER 1   The Parts of a Sentence   *(pages 2–9)*

Classifying Sentences

A **declarative sentence** makes a statement or expresses an opinion and ends with a period.

An **interrogative sentence** asks a question and ends with a question mark.

An **imperative sentence** makes a request or gives a command and ends with either a period or an exclamation point.

An **exclamatory sentence** expresses strong feeling and ends with an exclamation point.

◆ Using the following abbreviations, label each sentence. Add the correct end punctuation to each sentence.

declarative = D   imperative = IMP
interrogative = INT   exclamatory = EX

_____ 1. What an amazing place gold has had in legend and history

_____ 2. It was partly responsible for the rapid settlement of the West

_____ 3. Do you know when the Gold Rush started

_____ 4. Is gold still mined in the United States

_____ 5. Gold is a metal that never rusts or tarnishes

_____ 6. Read the story about Croesus

_____ 7. Wasn't he a wealthy ruler in ancient times

_____ 8. Yes, gold filled every room in the house

_____ 9. How proud he was of his golden throne

_____ 10. At the library look for pictures of his house

CHAPTER 1 **The Parts of a Sentence** *(pages 2–9)*

Mixed Practice: Kinds of Sentences

◆ Using the following abbreviations, label each sentence. Add the correct end punctuation to each sentence.

declarative = D   imperative = IMP
interrogative = INT   exclamatory = EX

_____ 1. Diamonds are the hardest natural stones on Earth

_____ 2. Are they used to cut gemstones

_____ 3. Where can you find diamonds

_____ 4. Most diamonds are mined in Africa

_____ 5. How beautiful they are

_____ 6. Diamonds are cut into many different shapes

_____ 7. Do you see the marquis-shaped stone

_____ 8. The brilliant, or round, cut is the most popular

_____ 9. Many diamonds have flaws

_____ 10. These flaws might make them look cloudy

_____ 11. A diamond's color is graded from yellow to white

_____ 12. Look at that white diamond

_____ 13. Carbon is under pressure for millions of years

_____ 14. Are there blue diamonds

_____ 15. You can buy irradiated diamonds of other colors

Name _____ Date _____

CHAPTER 2 ⬛ Nouns and Pronouns *(pages 10–17)*

Finding Nouns

A **noun** is a word that names a person, a place, a thing, or an idea.

◆ <u>Underline</u> each noun. (There are forty-five nouns.)

1. At one time dinosaurs were rulers of the earth.

2. Some of these creatures were as big as houses.

3. Other dinosaurs were as small as turkeys.

4. Many of these animals walked on two legs and used their hands to hold things.

5. Their brains were tiny—no bigger than a walnut.

6. We know about these reptiles from footprints and from fossils such as eggs, bones, and teeth.

7. Some bones have been formed into whole skeletons.

8. Experts can tell from fossils whether dinosaurs ate plants or meat.

9. Many questions, however, still have no answers.

10. One mystery is that we have no knowledge of what color these ancient creatures were.

11. Scientists guess that their colors might have been similar to those of living reptiles.

12. Another unsolved mystery concerns what caused dinosaurs to become extinct.

13. One popular theory is that Earth was struck by a large asteroid.

14. The impact would have sent a thick cloud of dust into the atmosphere.

CHAPTER 2 · Nouns and Pronouns *(pages 10–17)*

Using Specific Nouns

◆ Rewrite each sentence, replacing the underlined word or words with a more specific noun.

1. The big lizards are a very popular attraction at the museum.

   _____

   _____

2. Small humans seem to enjoy lizards and snakes the most.

   _____

   _____

3. My science teacher is an expert on dinosaurs.

   _____

   _____

4. Even my best friend likes learning about them.

   _____

   _____

5. Do you believe that a dinosaur could be the size of a small dog?

   _____

   _____

6. Would it be an interesting thought to keep a brachiosaurus for a protector?

   _____

   _____

CHAPTER 2   Nouns and Pronouns   *(pages 10–17)*

Finding Compound Nouns

A noun that includes more than one word is called a **compound noun**.

◆ <u>Underline</u> the compound nouns in each sentences below.

1. The police officer directed us to the picnic area.

2. Finally my great-grandfather was able to attend

3. My aunt brought her golden retriever.

4. Some of my cousins played on the sidewalk.

5. A cloudburst made all of us run for shelter.

6. Susie, my older sister, volunteered to be a baby-sitter while my aunts prepared the food.

7. My uncles played football.

8. After lunch we all watched the sailboats.

9. Fire ants ruined part of the picnic.

10. My cousin Katelyn asked me to be the maid of honor at her wedding next year.

CHAPTER 2   Nouns and Pronouns   *(pages 10–17)*

Writing Compound Nouns

◆ Rewrite each sentence, correcting the underlined compound noun. If the noun
is correct, make no changes. Use a dictionary to check your spelling.

1. My Aunt Sally used to be a <u>cheer-leader</u>.

   _____

   _____

2. Uncle Tom has been promoted to <u>firechief</u>.

   _____

   _____

3. By the next family reunion, I will have a new <u>brother in law</u>.

   _____

   _____

4. My dad got hurt sliding into <u>home plate</u>.

   _____

   _____

5. Mom attached the <u>fish-hook</u> to the end of the line.

   _____

   _____

CHAPTER 2   Nouns and Pronouns   *(pages 10–17)*

Finding Common and Proper Nouns

A **common noun** names any person, place, or thing.

A **proper noun** names a particular person, place, or thing.

◆ Underline each common noun <u>once</u> and each proper noun <u>twice</u>.

1. Buck did not read the newspapers, or he would have known about the problem in California.

2. When gold was found, prospectors rushed to the area.

3. They needed strong dogs with warm coats.

4. Buck was the son of a huge Saint Bernard.

5. He lived in a house owned by Judge Miller.

6. On the night that Buck was kidnapped, the judge was at a meeting of the Raisin Growers' Association.

7. The stolen dog would never return to his home.

8. He was sold to several different people.

9. Once he even pulled a sled that delivered mail between the towns of Dawson and Skagway.

10. After his last master died, he joined several wolves and roamed freely throughout the wilderness.

CHAPTER 2   **Nouns and Pronouns**   *(pages 10–17)*

Capitalizing Nouns

◆ Rewrite the following sentences, using capital letters for nouns correctly. If a sentence is correct, make no changes.

1. Jack London wrote the novel *The Call of the Wild*.

   _____

   _____

2. Buck's story takes place in california and alaska.

   _____

   _____

3. My favorite part of the Book was when buck joined the wolves and roamed the frozen Wilderness.

   _____

   _____

4. In one Part of the story, buck had to pull a sled with a tremendous Weight on it.

   _____

   _____

5. The whole story is told from the Dog's point of view.

   _____

   _____

CHAPTER 2   **Nouns and Pronouns**   *(pages 10–17)*

Mixed Practice: Common and Proper Nouns

◆ <u>Underline</u> each noun and label it *C* for a common noun or *P* for a proper noun.
(A date is considered a noun.)

1. In 1785, Thomas Pool presented the first circus in the United States.

2. It is not popcorn or elephants that have made circuses last all these years.

3. The excitement has come from original acts and unusual performers.

4. Five brothers once gathered some entertainers and traveled by wagons
to various cities.

5. Their name was Ringling.

6. Later P. T. Barnum offered three shows at the same time in different rings.

7. Americans always loved Emmett Kelly, a clown with a sad face.

8. Miguel Vazquez first performed four somersaults through the air to a catcher.

9. Tom Thumb was less than a yard tall.

10. President Lincoln invited him to the White House.

CHAPTER 2   Nouns and Pronouns   *(pages 10–17)*

Finding Antecedents

A **pronoun** is a word that takes the place of one or more nouns.

The noun that a pronoun replaces, or refers to, is called its **antecedent**.

◆ Draw an arrow to the antecedent of each underlined pronoun.

1. Michelle Akers, a star soccer player, is never sure how <u>she</u> will feel each day.

2. Michelle knows that <u>she</u> suffers from chronic fatigue syndrome.

3. The disease literally steals energy from <u>its</u> hosts.

4. Her coach, Tony DiCicco, says <u>he</u> is never sure how long Michelle will be able to play.

5. Michelle's family members say <u>they</u> worry about her health.

6. Still, Michelle is able to overcome <u>her</u> challenge and play great soccer for the U.S. women's team.

7. "<u>We</u> are a better team when Michelle is playing for us," says the coach.

8. In the 1996 Olympics, Michelle helped <u>her</u> team win the gold medal.

9. Michelle loves the sport, but it is a constant challenge for <u>her</u>.

10. "<u>I</u> don't know how long I'll be able to train or play in a match," says Michelle.

CHAPTER 2 **Nouns and Pronouns** *(pages 10–17)*

Finding Personal, Reflexive, and Intensive Pronouns

Personal pronouns take the place of one or more nouns. **Reflexive** and **intensive pronouns** refer to or emphasize a noun or another pronoun.

◆ <u>Underline</u> each personal, reflexive, and intensive pronoun. Label each one *P* for personal, *R* for reflexive, or *I* for intensive.

1. Our class has enjoyed itself learning about butterflies and moths in science.

2. I am writing a report about monarch butterflies.

3. I looked up their migration information on the Internet myself.

4. Did you know that butterflies touch plants with their feet because they have taste sensors in their feet?

5. When you see a butterfly hop from plant to plant, it is searching for a host plant for its eggs.

6. David Millard studies the habitats of butterflies and their predators.

7. Millard himself gave me much information for my science report.

8. Of all the reports about butterflies, I liked yours the best.

9. We want to plan and build a butterfly garden at our school.

10. Please be sure to share your drawings for the garden with me.

CHAPTER 2   **Nouns and Pronouns**   *(pages 10–17)*

Replacing Nouns with Pronouns

◆ Rewrite the following sentences, replacing some of the nouns with pronouns. Add reflexive or intensive pronouns wherever possible.

1. Mary said that Mary would help Charlotte hatch some butterfly eggs.

   _____

   _____

2. The students are going to present Mary with a special award for Mary's careful, accurate work with the butterflies.

   _____

   _____

3. David said that David would like to be able to present the special award to Mary.

   _____

   _____

4. Charlotte will take a picture of David and Mary in the new butterfly garden.

   _____

   _____

5. Will the students be able to enjoy the garden that the students helped to create?

   _____

   _____

CHAPTER 2　Nouns and Pronouns　(pages 10–17)

Finding Indefinite Pronouns

Indefinite pronouns refer to unnamed people, places, things, or ideas.

◆ <u>Underline</u> each indefinite pronoun.

1. Few know that flags first appeared in ancient China.

2. Most of the flags before then were actually poles with carved symbols on top.

3. Each of the units in the Roman army had a flag.

4. Someone discovered an Aztec flag made from feathers.

5. Many of the flags have important symbols on them.

6. All of the sailors learn the meanings of the flags.

7. Everyone has seen flags in sports.

8. Anyone who sees the red flag must stop immediately.

9. Most know a white flag means a single lap is left.

10. Anyone in the stands can see the checkered flag for the winner.

11. One of our legends states that Betsy Ross made the first American flag.

12. Everybody should stand when the flag passes by.

CHAPTER 2   Nouns and Pronouns   *(pages 10–17)*

Finding Pronouns

Demonstrative pronouns point out a specific person, place, thing, or idea.

Interrogative pronouns are used to ask questions.

◆ <u>Underline</u> each pronoun.

1. Either of the candidates will make a good class president for seventh grade.

2. What has Rebecca said about the campaign speech?

3. Who is running for treasurer?

4. All of the students are voting today.

5. These were found in the voting area.

6. Many voted for class historian.

7. What did Mrs. Thompson do with the extra ballots?

8. A campaign promise like this will be hard to keep.

9. Which is the ballot for the seventh-grade officers?

10. Whom did David tell about the new voting rules?

CHAPTER 2 Nouns and Pronouns *(pages 10–17)*

Writing Sentences

◆ Write a sentence that follows each direction. <u>Underline</u> the pronoun you use in each sentence.

◆ Use an interrogative pronoun to ask a question about an important election.

1. _____

_____

◆ Use a demonstrative pronoun to point out the voting booth.

2. _____

_____

◆ Use an indefinite pronoun to explain who is allowed to vote.

3. _____

_____

◆ Use an interrogative pronoun to find out the time that the winners will be announced.

4. _____

_____

◆ Use a demonstrative pronoun to point out the winner of the election.

5. _____

_____

CHAPTER 2   **Nouns and Pronouns**   *(pages 10–17)*

Mixed Practice: Pronouns

◆ <u>Underline</u> each pronoun.

1. No germs from the moon were found on Apollo 11 or its astronauts.

2. The doctors examined each of the astronauts.

3. This was the moment everyone had waited for.

4. They landed their spacecraft in the Pacific Ocean on July 24, 1969.

5. Which was the first astronaut to walk on the moon?

6. It was Neil Armstrong.

7. He said, "That's one small step for man, one giant leap for mankind."

8. That mission to the moon was a great human achievement.

9. Who did not land on the moon?

10. That was Michael Collins in orbit around the moon.

11. All of the astronauts made important discoveries.

12. These came from their mission.

13. A few of the discoveries included evidence of "moonquakes."

14. All of the data they collected was helpful to scientists.

15. Everybody was proud of the astronauts' success.

CHAPTER 3 **Verbs** *(pages 18–23)*

Finding Action Verbs

A **verb** is a word used to express an action or a state of being.

An **action verb** tells what action a subject is performing.

◆ <u>Underline</u> each action verb.

1. Every year dogsled drivers race across the frozen landscape of Alaska.

2. The course stretches more than a thousand miles from Anchorage to Nome.

3. Weather conditions often create severe hazards for the racers.

4. Snow and storms sometimes hide the trails.

5. Each driver carries snowshoes, a sleeping bag, and food for the dogs.

6. Drivers even take boots for the dogs' feet.

7. Veterinarians examine the dogs at checkpoints along the route.

8. Host families welcome the racers into their homes.

9. They feed the drivers and their dogs.

10. Most competitors complete the race within twelve or thirteen days.

11. A serious racer usually owns two or three different teams of dogs.

12. Some racers train all year long for the Iditarod.

13. Most teams enjoy the challenge of a good race.

14. A good "musher" has several strategies for the race.

15. People cheer for the victorious team.

CHAPTER 3   **Verbs**   *(pages 18–23)*

Revising with More Specific Verbs

◆ Replace the underlined verb in each sentence with a more specific verb.

1. The sleds <u>moved</u> across the frozen ground.

   _____

   _____

2. The dogs <u>went</u> past the spectators.

   _____

   _____

3. The injured dog <u>walked</u> to the rest station.

   _____

   _____

4. With plenty of time to spare, the winning team <u>crossed</u> over the finish line.

   _____

   _____

5. The weary sled dogs <u>came</u> into camp.

   _____

   _____

CHAPTER 3   **Verbs**   *(pages 18–23)*

Understanding Transitive and Intransitive Verbs

◆ <u>Underline</u> the verb in each sentence. Label the verb *T* for transitive or *I* for intransitive.

1. Jim Bowie lived in Tennessee and Louisiana during his childhood.

2. He inherited his parents' adventurous spirit.

3. During his childhood, he rode alligators.

4. Bowie learned from his mother.

5. He learned French and Spanish.

6. At the age of eighteen, Bowie sought his fortune.

7. He worked hard.

8. He made a profit from the work on his farm.

9. Jim Bowie received recognition as a frontiersman.

10. He arrived in Texas in 1828.

11. He searched Texas for silver.

12. He searched throughout Bexar County in Texas.

13. He led American settlers against the Mexican government.

14. Bowie's courage prevailed throughout the revolution.

15. Bowie defended the Alamo.

CHAPTER 3 Verbs *(pages 18–23)*

Finding Verb Phrases

A **verb phrase** is a main verb plus one or more helping verbs.

◆ <u>Underline</u> each verb phrase. Remember that a verb phrase may be interrupted by one or more words.

1. This rain shower should stop in a few minutes.

2. We will not go on a picnic in the rain.

3. Flowers have been appearing early this year.

4. The weather has not turned cooler today.

5. Rachel is planting her garden.

6. Have you seen any robins yet?

7. My parents will be cleaning the whole house soon.

8. We were planning a party this afternoon.

9. I haven't seen any dogwoods in bloom yet.

10. Will Kara be happy with the warmer weather?

CHAPTER 3   **Verbs**   *(pages 18–23)*

Using Verb Phrases in Sentences

◆ Rewrite the following sentences, adding a different helping verb to each one.

1. The dogwoods bloom in April in New Jersey.

   _____

   _____

2. Florida strawberries turn red in February.

   _____

   _____

3. Washington apples blush in the fall.

   _____

   _____

4. Peonies burst into bloom in May in Indiana.

   _____

   _____

5. Oranges sweeten in the frost.

   _____

   _____

6. Texas bluebonnets appear in the spring.

   _____

   _____

CHAPTER 3   Verbs   *(pages 18–23)*

Mixed Practice: Verbs

◆ Underline each verb or verb phrase.

1. The average tiger weighs between 396 and 583 pounds.

2. Do tigers live in Africa?

3. Tigers have lived in Asia for centuries.

4. Tigers are related to lions, leopards, and jaguars.

5. The tiger's distinctive black stripes provide excellent camouflage.

6. White tigers are not seen often.

7. The Bengal tiger is smaller than other tigers.

8. The male grows to an adult weight of 400 pounds.

9. Tiger babies are called cubs.

10. Cubs might stay with their parents for two years.

11. The father tiger does not help with the care of the cubs.

12. The Bengal tiger combines great power with lethal slyness.

13. A tiger can kill a water buffalo nearly four times its own weight.

14. They eat deer, wild pigs, and even monkeys.

15. Tigers have become more scarce in recent years.

CHAPTER 3   **Verbs**   *(pages 18–23)*

Finding Linking Verbs

A **linking verb** links the subject with another word that renames or describes the subject.

◆ Underline each linking verb.

1. Ships have been useful throughout history.

2. They might be the oldest form of transportation.

3. They are certainly popular today.

4. Lakes and rivers are home to many small boats.

5. A catamaran is a sailboat with twin hulls.

6. That boat can be fast.

7. The *USS Constitution* is a very old ship.

8. Steamships were the main form of transportation in the 1800s.

9. Could the lights on the cruise ship in the harbor be any brighter?

10. The largest ship is the oil tanker.

CHAPTER 3   **Verbs**   *(pages 18–23)*

Finding Linking Verbs

◆ <u>Underline</u> each linking verb. Then draw an arrow connecting the words that the verb links.

1. The giraffe is the world's tallest animal.

2. Earth's first space traveler was a dog.

3. In some parts of the world, cattle are still wild.

4. The whale is a mammal, not a fish.

5. Wild horses may be dangerous.

6. Most animals in Australia are unusual.

7. Dinosaurs must have been huge.

8. Birds could be descendants of dinosaurs.

9. The first horses were small.

CHAPTER 3   Verbs   *(pages 18–23)*

Finding Linking Verbs

◆ <u>Underline</u> each linking verb along with any helping verbs. Then draw an arrow connecting the words that the verb links.

1. Mozart's music appears difficult.

2. He became famous throughout Europe at a very young age.

3. His music does sound wonderful.

4. After the death of his father, Mozart's music turned darker.

5. Don Giovanni must have seemed scary to his audiences.

6. Mozart's music grew more complex.

7. His musical scores look perfect.

8. Did he ever feel successful?

9. Mozart did become ill toward the end of his life.

10. He and Haydn remained friendly for many years.

CHAPTER 3 **Verbs** *(pages 18–23)*

Revising Sentences with Linking Verbs

◆ Rewrite each sentence, replacing the underlined verb *was* with a different linking verb. In some sentences you will have to supply a helping verb.

1. Sherman <u>was</u> upset at the new score.

   _____

   _____

2. The music <u>was</u> difficult.

   _____

   _____

3. The conductor <u>was</u> firm about the selection.

   _____

   _____

4. Our first practice <u>was</u> awful.

   _____

   _____

5. Sherman <u>was</u> doubtful.

   _____

   _____

6. The selection <u>was</u> easier with each practice.

   _____

   _____

   _____

Name _____ Date _____

CHAPTER 3 **Verbs** *(pages 18–23)*

Linking Verb or Action Verb?

◆ <u>Underline</u> each verb. Then label each one *A* for action or *L* for linking.

1. The biggest dinosaur on Earth appeared smaller than a blue whale.

2. Blue whales stay calm in most situations.

3. Blue whales appeared after dinosaurs.

4. These huge animals stay underwater for periods as long as twenty minutes.

5. During the summer blue whales remain in arctic and antarctic waters.

6. In winter the blue whales migrate to subtropical waters.

7. Blue whales seem very intelligent.

8. Unfortunately, blue whales became an endangered species some time ago.

9. Many people look for a change in this situation.

10. What will become of the blue whale?

CHAPTER 3 Verbs *(pages 18–23)*

Writing Sentences with Linking and Action Verbs

◆ Write two sentences for each of the following verbs. First use the verb as a linking verb. Then use it as an action verb.

◆ look

1. _____

_____

2. _____

_____

◆ taste

3. _____

_____

4. _____

_____

◆ sound

5. _____

_____

6. _____

_____

Name _____ Date _____

CHAPTER 3 ▸ **Verbs** *(pages 18–23)*

Mixed Practice: Action and Linking Verbs

◆ <u>Underline</u> each verb along with any helping verbs. Then label each one *A* for action or *L* for linking.

1. Many people had not heard about El Niño before 1998.

2. *El niño* means "the boy" in Spanish.

3. El Niño has been responsible for unusual weather conditions around the world.

4. Florida was one state with El Niño problems.

5. In the winter months, the ground in Florida normally becomes dry.

6. The ground does not remain dry for long, though.

7. In May and June, the afternoon showers begin.

8. In 1998, the afternoon showers stayed away.

9. People looked for rain.

10. The ground grew drier.

11. By the end of June, the air smelled smoky.

12. Wildfires spread through grass and trees and across highways.

13. The situation was a dangerous one.

14. Some people lost their homes to the flames.

15. Finally, El Niño turned away.

CHAPTER 4   Adjectives and Adverbs   *(pages 24–31)*

Finding Adjectives

An **adjective** is a word that modifies a noun or pronoun.

◆ <u>Underline</u> each adjective. Then draw an arrow to the word it modifies.

1. A fierce hurricane begins over the ocean in the hot parts of the world.

2. Strong winds come from opposite directions and smash together.

3. Then the wild winds move in a circular pattern.

4. The calm center of the hurricane is called the eye.

5. The eye has light breezes and puffy clouds.

6. If the mighty winds of a hurricane hit land, they can cause severe damage.

7. Sturdy buildings have collapsed because of the huge waves or terrible winds of a severe hurricane.

8. With a hurricane comes heavy rain that often causes additional damage to property.

9. The rains often cause many rivers to overflow.

10. The powerful storm may weaken after it hits land.

CHAPTER 4 **Adjectives and Adverbs** *(pages 24–31)*

Adding Specific Adjectives

◆ Rewrite the following sentences, adding specific adjectives wherever possible.

1. The winds damaged the homes.

   _____

   _____

2. The boats rode out the storm on the ocean.

   _____

   _____

3. The storm ruined businesses.

   _____

   _____

4. People were without power for hours.

   _____

   _____

5. After the storm the winds calmed down.

   _____

   _____

CHAPTER 4   Adjectives and Adverbs   *(pages 24–31)*

Finding Adjectives

◆ <u>Underline</u> each adjective. Then draw an arrow to the word or words it modifies. (Do not include articles.)

1. Georgia O'Keeffe was one of the most original artists of the early twentieth century.

2. Her famous flower paintings, large and colorful, appeared in the art scene of the mid-1920s.

3. She also painted precise and geometric city scenes.

4. In 1929, she moved to New Mexico, where she painted beautiful and unusual still lifes and landscapes.

5. Her paintings reflected the colorful desert of the Southwest.

6. A teacher once told Georgia that her drawings were small and dark.

7. As a result, she always painted everything large and bright.

8. Her unique style increased her popularity as an artist.

9. She enjoyed a long career.

10. Her bold, inspirational paintings are still popular today.

CHAPTER 4   **Adjectives and Adverbs**   *(pages 24–31)*

Using Commas with Adjectives

◆ Add or remove commas between adjectives if necessary. If a sentence is correct, make no changes.

1. Our favorite, art teacher took us to the museum today.

2. She wanted us to see the museum's famous new collection of Georgia O'Keeffe paintings.

3. At the entrance a large colorful poster of a poppy amazed us.

4. The bright, red flower dominated the exhibit.

5. I found O'Keeffe's bold unique paintings very beautiful.

CHAPTER 4   Adjectives and Adverbs   *(pages 24–31)*

Finding Adjectives

◆ <u>Underline</u> each proper adjective. Then draw an arrow to the word it modifies.

1. Mr. Taylor told us, in his best English accent, that we would be participating in the school's cultural fair.

2. Nancy Coleman brought a German clock for our booth.

3. I saw wonderful African masks at the booth next to ours.

4. We ate Greek food at the fair.

5. While at the festival, José bought a souvenir at the Italian booth.

6. The Chinese embroidery that Ming brought was very delicate.

7. The local Republican candidate helped us open the fair.

8. We could hear the Mexican musicians playing mariachi music.

9. A Congressional representative also came to the fair.

10. She was surprised to win a Hawaiian vacation at the raffle.

CHAPTER 4 **Adjectives and Adverbs** *(pages 24–31)*

Capitalizing Proper Adjectives

◆ Rewrite the following sentences, capitalizing each proper adjective. If a sentence is correct, make no changes.

1. My mother can speak the french language very well.

   _____

   _____

2. Did you get to see the irish dancers?

   _____

   _____

3. My favorite part of the fair was the performance of the Scottish pipers.

   _____

   _____

4. John liked the spanish flamenco dancers.

   _____

   _____

5. Did Sara like the african storyteller?

   _____

   _____

CHAPTER 4   **Adjectives and Adverbs**   *(pages 24–31)*

Adjective or Noun?

◆ Label each underlined word *A* for adjective or *N* for noun.

1. How many gallons of <u>paint</u> will we need for the dugout?

2. I will need a new <u>spring</u> jacket before we start practice.

3. The <u>baseball</u> soared over center field and into the bleachers.

4. On which <u>train</u> car will the team eat?

5. Finding time to practice can be a <u>major</u> problem for me.

6. Can the <u>paint</u> stains be removed from the dugout floor?

7. The <u>train</u> was empty except for our team.

8. This <u>spring</u> we have had better practices.

9. Our coach was a <u>major</u> in the army.

10. Why did you join the <u>baseball</u> team this year?

CHAPTER 4 **Adjectives and Adverbs** *(pages 24–31)*

Writing Sentences with Nouns and Adjectives

◆ Write two sentences for each of the following words. Use the word as an adjective in the first sentence. Use the word as a noun in the second sentence.

◆ radio

1. _____

_____

2. _____

_____

◆ city

3. _____

_____

4. _____

_____

◆ art

5. _____

_____

6. _____

_____

CHAPTER 4　Adjectives and Adverbs　*(pages 24–31)*

Adjective or Pronoun?

◆ Label each underlined word with *A* for an adjective or *P* for a pronoun.

1. <u>Few</u> people realize that Wilbur and Orville Wright made bicycles before airplanes.

2. They experimented with <u>many</u> designs before their historic flight at Kitty Hawk.

3. <u>Which</u> brother made the first flight?

4. <u>Few</u> understand the dangers of the first flight.

5. <u>That</u> airplane of the Wright brothers began as a glider.

6. <u>What</u> challenges did they face in December 1903?

7. <u>Both</u> brothers continued to make airplanes.

8. <u>Many</u> wanted to fly after Wilbur and Orville's successful flight.

9. <u>What</u> did Wilbur do?

10. A <u>few</u> people helped the Wright brothers with their first flight on December 17, 1903.

Name _____ Date _____

Writing Sentences with Adjectives and Pronouns

◆ Write two sentences for each of the following words. Use the word as an adjective in the first sentence. Use the word as a pronoun in the second sentence.

◆ some

1. _____

   _____

2. _____

   _____

◆ these

3. _____

   _____

4. _____

   _____

◆ this

5. _____

   _____

6. _____

   _____

CHAPTER 4 **Adjectives and Adverbs** *(pages 24–31)*

Mixed Practice: Adjectives

◆ <u>Underline</u> each adjective. Then draw an arrow to the word it modifies. Do not include articles. (There are thirty-five adjectives.)

1. Gorillas, shy and gentle, are peaceful animals.

2. A gorilla may reach a height of six feet.

3. The arms, long and powerful, almost touch the ground.

4. Gorillas live in small family groups.

5. They roam many miles each day in search of food for their family group.

6. They eat fruits and green leafy plants.

7. Toward evening they construct several platforms for sleeping.

8. The male leader sleeps on the bottom platform of the structure.

9. The leader is the strongest and protects the other members of the group.

10. The females and the young gorillas sleep on the top platforms on high branches.

11. Every day gorillas build new shelters.

12. Gorillas with short hair live in the hot, damp areas of the Congo River valley.

13. The faces of these gorillas are hairless and shiny.

14. Gorillas with coarse hair live in the cool air of the African mountains.

15. Most gorillas live in and around the central part of Africa.

Name _____ Date _____

....

Finding Adverbs

An **adverb** is a word that modifies a verb, an adjective, or another adverb.

◆ Underline each adverb and draw an arrow to the word or words it modifies.

1. Our track team rarely loses.

2. Stephanie rushed forward to the finish line.

3. Lately the team has been practicing in the morning.

4. Danny was quickly tying his shoes.

5. Did you really forget your discus?

6. Finally the meet has begun.

7. Mira is practicing the long jump again.

8. We have looked everywhere for a new stopwatch.

9. Ellis will never run there.

10. Don't stop now!

11. You should always stretch thoroughly.

12. Sometimes I also run hurdles.

13. We often run here.

14. Nancy always jumps superbly.

15. Franklin hasn't finished the shot put yet.

CHAPTER 4   Adjectives and Adverbs   *(pages 24–31)*

Writing Sentences with Adverbs

◆ Using adverbs, write sentences that follow each direction. <u>Underline</u> each adverb.

◆ Describe how a friend talks.

1. _____

_____

◆ Describe how a detective enters a dark, scary house.

2. _____

_____

◆ Describe how a toddler walks.

3. _____

_____

◆ Describe how you do your homework.

4. _____

_____

◆ Describe how you eat spaghetti.

5. _____

_____

CHAPTER 4 **Adjectives and Adverbs** *(pages 24–31)*

Finding Adverbs

◆ <u>Underline</u> each adverb. Draw an arrow to the word it modifies.

1. The actors were extremely nervous.

2. You should whisper very quietly backstage.

3. It rained quite often during the month of outdoor performances.

4. The actors were truly responsible.

5. Rita arrived too early for her cue.

6. Rain fell quite heavily for an hour before the show.

7. Lenny has an unusually powerful voice.

8. The pace was moving rather slowly.

9. The music was exceptionally loud.

10. The play seemed somewhat long.

11. The audience is usually enthusiastic.

12. Joyce is often absent from practice.

13. The crowd grew curiously silent after the last act.

14. This play is strangely familiar.

15. Despite the problems the actors appeared totally calm.

CHAPTER 4   Adjectives and Adverbs   *(pages 24–31)*

Writing Sentences with Adverbs

◆ Use each word as an adverb in a sentence. Then rewrite the sentence, putting the adverb in a different part of the sentence.

◆ calmly

1. _____

   _____

2. _____

   _____

◆ never

3. _____

   _____

4. _____

   _____

◆ quickly

5. _____

   _____

6. _____

   _____

CHAPTER 4 · Adjectives and Adverbs (pages 24–31)

Mixed Practice: Adverbs

◆ Underline each adverb. Draw an arrow to the word or words it modifies.

1. Giraffes glide gracefully and noiselessly across the plains of Kenya in Africa.

2. There they search hungrily and eagerly for the acacia tree.

3. A family of giraffes will often feed from the same tree.

4. Drinking water is the most difficult job for a giraffe.

5. This unusually tall animal drinks slowly and awkwardly.

6. Carefully it bends its knees and its neck and laps cautiously at the cool water.

7. The giraffe's very long neck contains the same number of bones as the neck of a guinea pig.

8. These neck bones are much longer in the giraffe than in the guinea pig.

9. The neck bones are also bigger in the giraffe.

10. The giraffe seldom uses its quite unusual voice.

11. Ordinarily, a giraffe will not attack other creatures.

12. Daily a giraffe will eat acacia leaves on the grassy plains.

13. Other animals rarely threaten the giraffe's survival.

14. Lions occasionally bother giraffes.

15. Sometimes visitors to Kenya's national parks see the giraffes.

CHAPTER 4 **Adjectives and Adverbs** *(pages 24–31)*

Mixed Practice: Adjectives and Adverbs

◆ Underline each adjective <u>once</u> and adverb <u>twice</u>. Draw an arrow to the word each modifies.

1. Venus is often visible in the evening sky.

2. Some people worry about comets.

3. Several planets can be easily seen in the night sky.

4. Many objects in the night sky have been given Latin names from Roman myths.

5. Orion, the hunter, always chases his prey across the winter sky.

6. The earth spins slowly on its axis.

7. Suddenly the brilliant supernova disappeared.

8. The star Vega burns brightly in the constellation Lyra.

9. Usually the middle of August is a good time to see summer stars.

10. Summer is often the best time to see the Milky Way.

11. Many people mistake it for a weather cloud.

12. The Big Dipper is usually identifiable.

13. Frequently you can see Mars, Jupiter, or Saturn.

14. They look like bright stars, but they do not twinkle.

Name _____ Date _____

CHAPTER 5 Prepositions, Conjunctions, & Interjections

(pages 32–37)

....

Supplying Prepositions

A **preposition** is a word that shows the relationship between a noun or a pronoun and another word in the sentence.

◆ Write two prepositions that could fill each blank in the following sentences.

1. The narrow road ran ___ the cliffs.

   _____

2. A huge boulder was lying ___ the path.

   _____

3. The scouts camped ___ the lake.

   _____

4. I found my compass ___ the stream.

   _____

5. Kathleen found the missing backpack ___ the tent.

   _____

6. Our guide looked for a bear ___ the bushes.

   _____

7. A huge falcon flew ___ the clouds.

   _____

8. The hikers climbed ___ the rocks.

   _____

CHAPTER 5 Prepositions, Conjunctions, & Interjections

(pages 32–37)

Finding Prepositional Phrases

A **prepositional phrase** is a group of words made up of a preposition, its object, and any words that modify the object.

◆ Underline each prepositional phrase.

1. The Galapagos Islands are located near Ecuador.

2. They cover an area of 3,029 square miles.

3. The islands contain many animals of interest.

4. You can find turtles throughout the islands.

5. Marine iguanas are sometimes found in junkyards.

6. During his visit in 1835, Charles Darwin observed many interesting animals.

7. According to Darwin, each of the islands is inhabited by vastly different species.

8. Centuries before Darwin's famous visit, ancient people traveled to the islands.

9. Many tourists enjoy the Galapagos Islands for their different animals and plants.

10. Certain species of penguins live on one of the islands near the equator!

CHAPTER 5   Prepositions, Conjunctions, & Interjections

(pages 32–37)

Finding Prepositional Phrases

◆ <u>Underline</u> each preposition and draw an arrow to its object. (There are fifteen prepositional phrases.)

1. The trunk of an elephant is like a hose.

2. Elephants inhale water through their trunks.

3. Then they curl their trunks and shoot the water into their mouths.

4. Elephants eat food in a similar way.

5. With their trunks elephants also spray water onto their backs.

6. They like water and can swim for six hours.

7. During the hottest hours, elephants often huddle under trees.

8. Elephants also throw mud over their bodies.

9. With their trunks elephants can break large branches from trees.

10. In a wildlife park, an elephant can live for sixty-five years.

Name _____ Date _____

(pages 32–37)

Writing Sentences

◆ Write five sentences about an animal that lives in the wild. Use at least one prepositional phrase in each sentence.

1. _____

   _____

2. _____

   _____

3. _____

   _____

4. _____

   _____

5. _____

   _____

Name _____ Date _____

Preposition or Adverb?

◆ Label each underlined word *P* for preposition or *A* for adverb.

1. We drove <u>through</u> Chicago in less than an hour.

2. The mountains stood a long way <u>off</u>.

3. We ate our lunch <u>near</u> Lake Michigan.

4. Every morning Dad checked <u>around</u> the car.

5. Did you drive straight <u>through</u>?

6. Lisa left the tickets <u>behind</u>.

7. My suitcase rolled <u>off</u> the roof rack.

8. Don't come <u>near</u>, for I have to focus the camera.

9. Did you look <u>around</u>?

10. The spare tire may have rolled <u>behind</u> that bush.

Name _____ Date _____

(pages 32–37)

Writing Sentences with Prepositional Phrases and Adverbs

◆ Write two sentences for each of the following words. Use the word as a preposition in the first sentence and as an adverb in the second sentence.

◆ in

1. _____

_____

2. _____

_____

◆ across

3. _____

_____

4. _____

_____

◆ below

5. _____

_____

6. _____

_____

CHAPTER 5　Prepositions, Conjunctions, & Interjections

(pages 32–37)

Mixed Practice: Prepositional Phrases

◆ Underline the prepositional phrases in the following paragraphs.

1. Does a monster really hide in Loch Ness? For many centuries people have reportedly seen this strange creature. The Loch Ness monster first had its picture taken in 1934. Dr. R. K. Wilson was driving along the shore. Suddenly he saw movement in the water and grabbed his camera. The result is a very famous, very blurry photograph of a mysterious object. The fuzzy picture just *might* show a strange animal with an extremely long neck. Some people, however, are not convinced by this photograph.

2. With special underwater cameras, scientists have searched more recently for the Loch Ness monster. Unfortunately, the new pictures also show little except fuzzy shapes. Most scientists do not believe in the monster. Possible explanations for the monster include a large fish, an unusual wave, and a giant seal. Believers, though, think that a dinosaur may have survived from prehistoric times. Without better evidence the Loch Ness mystery will remain unsolved.

CHAPTER 5   Prepositions, Conjunctions, & Interjections

(pages 32–37)

Finding Conjunctions and Interjections

A **conjunction** connects words or groups of words.

An **interjection** is a word that expresses strong feeling.

◆ <u>Underline</u> each conjunction or interjection and label it *C* or *I*.

1. Either Sam or David will have to bait my hook.

2. You and I are responsible for the fish.

3. Wow! Did you see the size of the fish Susan caught?

4. Nani will bake or broil the fresh fish.

5. The fish were biting, but no one caught any.

6. Both bass and trout are tasty.

7. Ugh! Someone removed the fish from the cooler.

8. Lures and hooks are scattered everywhere.

9. Neither Tom nor Cherri could clean the fish.

10. Oh, you should have seen the big one that got away!

CHAPTER 5 Prepositions, Conjunctions, & Interjections

(pages 32–37)

Revising Sentences with Conjunctions

◆ Rewrite the following passage, removing any conjunctions, rewriting sentences
  as necessary. Notice how different the passage is without conjunctions!

> Besides, he thought, next year he would be bigger and could walk faster
> and get to school before it started and wouldn't be laughed at. And when he
> wasn't dead-tired from walking home from school, his father would let him
> hunt with Sounder. Having both school and Sounder would be mighty good,
> but if he couldn't have school, he could always have Sounder.
>
> —William Armstrong, *Sounder*

_____

_____

_____

_____

_____

_____

_____

_____

CHAPTER 5   Prepositions, Conjunctions, & Interjections

(pages 32–37)

....

Determining Parts of Speech

◆ Label each underlined word with its part of speech, using the following abbreviations:

noun = N	adverb = ADV
preposition = PREP	verb = V
adjective = ADJ	pronoun = PRO
conjunction = CONJ	interjection = INTER

1. As a <u>young</u> child, Clara proved to be good <u>at</u> studies.

2. <u>Everyone</u> loved her, <u>and</u> her family encouraged her many interests.

3. Her father <u>sometimes</u> told her exciting adventure stories.

4. <u>Oh</u>, did you know that she was born on Christmas day?

5. <u>She</u> owned several pets, including a turkey and a snapping turtle that <u>frequently</u> frightened the other children.

6. <u>Well</u>, one day her brother's dog <u>became</u> sick; only Clara was able to heal it.

7. Soon children from other farms <u>brought</u> their <u>dogs</u> to Clara.

8. As a young <u>woman</u>, she cared for wounded soldiers <u>during</u> the Civil War.

9. Many soldiers knew her <u>only</u> as "The Angel of Battlefield" and a <u>gentle</u> voice.

10. In later years, <u>Clara</u> <u>founded</u> the American Red Cross.

Name _____ Date _____

CHAPTER 5   Prepositions, Conjunctions, & Interjections

(pages 32–37)

Determining Parts of Speech

◆ Label each underlined word with its part of speech, using the following
abbreviations:

noun = *N*	adverb = *ADV*	conjunction = *CONJ*
preposition = *PREP*	verb = *V*	interjection = *INTER*
adjective = *ADJ*	pronoun = *PRO*	

1.   The study of names <u>is</u> <u>fun</u>. <u>During</u> the Middle Ages, <u>most</u> people <u>had</u> only a first name. <u>That</u> was <u>fine</u>, as long as <u>everyone</u> stayed in <u>his</u> or her village. Cities were <u>finally</u> formed, <u>and</u> people moved <u>from</u> place to place. <u>Five</u> Marys in the same place <u>became</u> confusing. The solution <u>was</u> easy. Most people added information to their names. <u>They</u> used one of four methods.

2.   First, a <u>son</u> might take the <u>name</u> of his father. As a result, Henry would become Henry, son of John. <u>Through</u> time, this became Henry Johnson.

3.   Second, <u>people</u> were named <u>for</u> some of their features. A strong person could be named Henry Strong or Henry Hardy. A person with <u>red</u> hair might take the last name of Reed or Reid. The names Wise, Grim, Moody, and Sharp came about <u>for</u> the same reason.

4.   Third, people became identified with the place <u>of</u> their birth. The Woods <u>or</u> the Atwoods, for example, <u>lived</u> near a forest. The Fairbanks family would have come from the edge of a <u>lovely</u> river or stream.

5.   Fourth, people were named for their <u>occupations</u>. A town's <u>blacksmith</u> might be called Henry the Smith. <u>Later</u> this would become Henry Smith. The roofmaker would be called Henry Thatcher, <u>but</u> the village grain <u>merchant</u> would be Henry Miller.

Name _____ Date _____

(pages 32–37)

Writing Sentences with Different Parts of Speech

◆ Write sentences that follow the directions.

◆ Use *baseball* as a noun and an adjective.

1. _____

   _____

2. _____

   _____

◆ Use *this* as a pronoun and an adjective.

3. _____

   _____

4. _____

   _____

◆ Use *one* as a pronoun and an adjective.

5. _____

   _____

6. _____

   _____

CHAPTER 6   **Complements**   *(pages 38–43)*

Finding Direct Objects

A **direct object** is a noun or pronoun that answers the question *What?* or *Whom?* after an action verb.

◆ <u>Underline</u> each direct object.

1. Ducks will lay eggs only in the morning.

2. You can make eleven omelets with an ostrich egg.

3. Chimpanzees use twigs and rocks as tools.

4. A robin has almost three thousand feathers.

5. Did you see eagles on your trip to the lake?

6. Some earthworms have ten hearts.

7. Lemon sharks grow new teeth every two weeks.

8. One type of spider can spin a web in twenty minutes.

9. Bats squeal and use their ears for navigation.

10. Will a wolf abandon its pups?

11. Have you seen the bats under the bridge?

12. Every spring the bats use the bridge as a nursery.

13. A mother bat raises one baby at a time.

14. At night the bats eat insects.

15. They prefer moths and other pests.

CHAPTER 6 **Complements** *(pages 38–43)*

Writing Sentences with Direct Objects

◆ Write a sentence that answers each question. Then underline each direct object in your sentences.

◆ What do you see directly in front of you?

1. _____

   _____

◆ Whom did you visit recently?

2. _____

   _____

◆ What did you eat for dinner last night?

3. _____

   _____

◆ How many pencils and pens do you have?

4. _____

   _____

◆ What kinds of books do you like best?

5. _____

   _____

CHAPTER 6 **Complements** *(pages 38–43)*

Finding Indirect Objects

An **indirect object** is a noun or pronoun that answers the question *To or for whom?* or *To or for what?* after an action verb.

◆ Underline each indirect object.

1. We fed the ducks bread crumbs.

2. Dad cooked us hamburgers on the grill.

3. Sara showed us the delicious dessert.

4. Will you pass me the ketchup?

5. My mom found everyone at the picnic a shady spot for lunch.

6. Did Steve make Mary that fried chicken?

7. You must give Rosemarie and him some lemonade.

8. Have you given Sandra the recipe?

9. Please take your sister this cookie.

10. Susan will reserve us the shelter for our next picnic.

11. Our teacher read the class several biographies of famous mathematicians.

12. Ms. Gomez taught our class the Pythagorean theorem.

13. Then she showed several students a picture of Archimedes.

14. The picture gave me a more vivid impression of him.

15. Archimedes gave Syracuse and Sicily the invention of the catapult.

CHAPTER 6   Complements   *(pages 38–43)*

Revising Sentences with Indirect Objects

◆ Choose any five of the sentences from the preceding exercise to rewrite without indirect objects. In some cases you may have to write two sentences to convey the same meaning, or you may have to use a prepositional phrase.

1. _____

_____

2. _____

_____

3. _____

_____

4. _____

_____

5. _____

_____

CHAPTER 6 **Complements** *(pages 38–43)*

Mixed Practice: Direct and Indirect Objects

◆ <u>Underline</u> each complement in the following sentences. Then label each one *DO* for direct object or *IO* for indirect object.

1. Have you ever eaten an artichoke or an avocado?

2. I tasted both at the food fair.

3. Anton cooked everyone a Mexican meal.

4. Grandmother made Martina and me sweet potato candy.

5. For decoration, people sometimes put flowers on cakes.

6. Please pass us the eggrolls and the chopsticks from the Asian display.

7. Did you show him the stuffed pitas?

8. Two new students were nibbling scones and biscuits at the fair.

9. Anna showed Peter and Maria her cooking project.

10. Mrs. Pallone kept the same booth as last year.

11. The judges awarded Chet first prize for most unusual recipe.

12. Rona saved me a seat at a table in the German tent.

13. Make your little brother and sister some baklava.

14. We bought Flora some fortune cookies.

15. I brought Will and Betsy a piece of fresh-baked shortbread.

CHAPTER 6 Complements *(pages 38–43)*

Finding Predicate Nominatives

A **predicate nominative** is a noun or a pronoun that follows a linking verb and identifies, renames, or explains the subject.

◆ <u>Underline</u> each predicate nominative.

1. Diamonds are extremely hard and rare stones.

2. The prairie sunsets were spectacular sights.

3. Those huge trees are maples.

4. The main resources of South Asia are soil, water, and climate.

5. The longest rivers in the world are the Amazon and the Nile.

6. The land in Pennsylvania may be a good source of coal.

7. Saudi Arabia remains a major producer of oil.

8. Rhode Island is the smallest state.

9. My favorite countries are the United States and Mexico.

10. California has become one of the candidates for a major earthquake.

CHAPTER 6 **Complements** *(pages 38–43)*

Supplying Predicate Nominatives

◆ Write a predicate nominative that completes each sentence. Then <u>underline</u> the word it renames. If you use a pronoun as a predicate nominative, use only *I, you, he, she, it, we,* or *they.*

1. My favorite musician is _____.

2. My favorite musical instrument is the _____.

3. My brother Roy will become a _____.

4. The instrument featured is a _____.

5. Their soloist is a _____.

6. Eric is a _____.

7. Mrs. Davis is my _____.

8. The soloist in Sunday's concert will be _____.

9. My favorite song is _____.

10. The drummer in the band is _____.

CHAPTER 6 **Complements** *(pages 38–43)*

Revising Sentences with Predicate Nominatives

◆ Rewrite the following sentences so that they contain a different predicate nominative.

1. When I grow up, I want to be a musician.

   _____

   _____

2. My favorite instrument is the piano.

   _____

   _____

3. My favorite types of music are classical and jazz.

   _____

   _____

4. One of the best schools for the study of music is Juilliard.

   _____

   _____

CHAPTER 6 Complements *(pages 38–43)*

Finding Predicate Adjectives

A **predicate adjective** is an adjective that follows a linking verb and modifies the subject.

◆ <u>Underline</u> each predicate adjective. (Some sentences may have a compound predicate adjective.)

1. That polar bear is hungry again.

2. Its claws are long and sharp.

3. Polar bears seem cuddly.

4. The Arctic winter is dark and cold.

5. The mother polar bear appears thin after the long winter season.

6. The den seems warm in the spring.

7. The bears appear curious about the scientists.

8. That huge bear is dangerous.

9. The ice is bright and slippery.

10. The bear's head looks long and pointy.

CHAPTER 6 **Complements** *(pages 38–43)*

Supplying Predicate Adjectives

◆ Write a predicate adjective that completes each sentence. Avoid overused adjectives such as *good*, *nice*, and *wonderful*.

1. All of the original poems that Terry wrote are _____.

2. During her oral presentation, Dawn looked _____.

3. The poet was _____.

4. After waiting thirty minutes for the presentation
   to start, the class became _____.

5. After finishing her writing projects, Natalie
   always seemed so _____.

6. After her presentation, Alana appeared _____.

7. That new poem sounds _____.

8. Kyle's volume is too _____.

9. Both Ray and Alice were _____.

10. Many of the original poems from this year's
    class sound _____.

Name _____ Date _____

CHAPTER 6 **Complements** *(pages 38–43)*

Writing Sentences with Predicate Nominatives and Adjectives

◆ Write four sentences about a poem you like. Include a predicate nominative in two of the sentences and a predicate adjective in the other two sentences. Label each complement *PN* for predicate nominative or *PA* for predicate adjective.

1. _____

_____

_____

2. _____

_____

_____

3. _____

_____

_____

4. _____

_____

_____

CHAPTER 6 ◾ Complements ◾ *(pages 38–43)*

Mixed Practice: Complements

◆ <u>Underline</u> each complement in the following sentences. Label each
  complement *PN* for predicate nominative or *PA* for predicate adjective.

1. Television became very popular in the 1950s.

2. *Howdy Doody* was a favorite children's program of the time.

3. The characters Howdy Doody and Clarabelle the Clown were comical.

4. For more than twenty million teenagers, the most popular show in the late 1950s
   was *American Bandstand.*

5. Davy Crockett was one of the most admired TV characters of the decade.

6. Davy Crockett was a frontiersman.

7. Popular clothes for boys during those years were chino pants and
   motorcycle jackets.

8. Pedal pushers, bobby socks, and poodle skirts were fashionable for girls.

9. Hula hoops became a fad in 1958.

10. TV dinners in little aluminum foil dishes first became popular in 1954.

Name _____ Date _____

Finding Prepositional Phrases

A **prepositional phrase** is a group of words that begins with a preposition, ends with a noun or a pronoun, and is used as an adjective or adverb.

◆ <u>Underline</u> each prepositional phrase.

1. Cesar Chavez was born in 1927 in the Southwest near Yuma, Arizona.

2. He would later become an important leader of farm workers.

3. After the stock market crash in 1929, the Chavez family became migrant farm workers.

4. Chavez enlisted in the Navy during World War II.

5. In 1952, he was recruited by Fred Ross as a worker for the Community Service Organization.

6. With the CSO, Cesar Chavez worked for the aid of the poor.

7. By 1958, Cesar Chavez had become the national director of the CSO.

8. He resigned from the CSO in 1962 and started a farm workers' union.

9. Cesar Chavez changed the system through nonviolent means.

10. With his dedication, he helped many migrant farm workers.

CHAPTER 7   **Phrases**   *(pages 44–49)*

Finding Adjective Phrases

An **adjective phrase** is a prepositional phrase that modifies a noun or pronoun.

◆ <u>Underline</u> each adjective phrase.

1. The most famous city in France is Paris.

2. Paris is the capital of France.

3. It is one of the largest French cities.

4. Paris is also one of the major European cities.

5. Each of the twenty districts within Paris has its own mayor.

6. The most famous painting at the Louvre is the *Mona Lisa*.

7. The street in front of the Louvre is called the Triumphal Way.

8. A famous architect completed a renovation of the Louvre.

9. The view from the Eiffel Tower is breathtaking.

10. The sidewalk beneath the tower is a popular tourist area.

CHAPTER 7   Phrases   *(pages 44–49)*

Finding Adjective Phrases

◆ <u>Underline</u> each adjective phrase. Then draw an arrow to the word that the phrase modifies.

1. The lake beyond those hills has an excellent sailing course.

2. One of my friends owns a sailboat.

3. The dock across the lake is vacant.

4. Six friends on the committee organized a pancake breakfast for the sailors.

5. The sailboat with the torn sail left the race.

6. The day after tomorrow should be a good time for us.

7. The sails on our boat have double rows of stitches.

8. The three smallest boats at the race were the fastest boats.

9. The best sailor on the water is Toby.

10. The McFarlins own the boat beside ours.

CHAPTER 7   **Phrases**   *(pages 44–49)*

Writing Sentences with Adjective Phrases

◆ Write a sentence that uses each of the following prepositional phrases as an adjective phrase. Remember to place each phrase after the noun or the pronoun it modifies.

◆ of students

1. _____

_____

◆ with the green stripes

2. _____

_____

◆ near the ocean

3. _____

_____

◆ on the lake

4. _____

_____

◆ from my aunt

5. _____

_____

CHAPTER 7 **Phrases** *(pages 44–49)*

Finding Misplaced Adjective Phrases

◆ Underline each misplaced adjective phrase.

1. Our teacher in the cafeteria talked about good manners.

2. The librarian gave books without library cards to the children.

3. Our school has many activities for students with no sports emphasis.

4. The school has an excellent academic record beyond that street.

5. That unusually large classroom is vacant across the hall.

6. The best teacher is Mrs. Emerson in the English department.

7. The shady area is called the Peace Garden in front of our school.

8. That student was lost from another school.

9. The principal handed passes to the students for a local amusement park.

10. The boy was shouting with the backpack on one shoulder.

CHAPTER 7 **Phrases** *(pages 44–49)*

Correcting Sentences with Misplaced Adjective Phrases

◆ Choose five sentences from the preceding exercise to rewrite with the adjective phrases in the proper place.

1. _____

_____

2. _____

_____

3. _____

_____

4. _____

_____

5. _____

_____

CHAPTER 7 **Phrases** *(pages 44–49)*

Finding Adverb Phrases

An **adverb phrase** is a prepositional phrase that is used mainly to modify a verb.

◆ Underline each adverb phrase.

1. A snail lives inside a tough spiral shell.

2. On its slow travels, a snail drags its shell on its back.

3. A snail creeps on a large footlike structure.

4. Many snails have a slimy fluid under this foot.

5. With this fluid snails can crawl up vertical surfaces.

6. A snail can climb safely over a razor blade.

7. In a dangerous situation, a snail pulls its head inside its shell.

8. Within its tough shell, the snail hides from most enemies.

9. Land snails usually live in shady, damp places.

10. With a long, toothed "tongue," a snail scrapes its food off surfaces.

CHAPTER 7   Phrases *(pages 44–49)*

Finding Adverb Phrases

◆ <u>Underline</u> each adverb phrase. Then draw an arrow to the word or words each adverb phrase modifies.

1. The baseball whizzed by the batter.

2. A hush descended over the crowd.

3. Within a few hours, David Cone pitched a perfect baseball game.

4. David Cone looked around the baseball field carefully.

5. The catcher sent the signals across the field.

6. Toward the eighth inning, the fans became quiet.

7. Anxious faces appeared in the dugout.

8. David Cone pitched the entire game without a base runner.

9. After the game he celebrated and thanked the fans.

10. This perfect baseball game will live forever in sports history.

CHAPTER 7 **Phrases** *(pages 44–49)*

Punctuating Adverb Phrases

◆ Add or delete commas so the adverb phrases are punctuated correctly in the sentences below. If a sentence is correct, make no changes.

1. In Cooperstown, you will find the Baseball Hall of Fame.

2. Until last week, I had no idea where it was.

3. On several occasions, Joe has visited there.

4. In the spring my family toured it.

5. In the famous hall we learned about the players.

CHAPTER 7   **Phrases**   *(pages 44–49)*

Mixed Practice: Prepositional Phrases

◆ <u>Underline</u> each prepositional phrase. Then label each one *ADJ* for adjective or *ADV* for adverb.

1. Basketball was invented in 1891.

2. At the time no major sport was played in winter.

3. A man at a Massachusetts YMCA school had a wonderful idea.

4. This person was James A. Naismith, the father of basketball.

5. Basketball provided a sport between the football season and the baseball season.

6. The origin of its name is an interesting story.

7. Naismith had no money for fancy equipment.

8. In a hall he nailed peach baskets on opposite walls.

9. The game's name came from the peach baskets.

10. Another necessary piece of equipment for the new game was a tall ladder.

11. The bottoms of the peach baskets were not removed.

12. At the start everyone used an old soccer ball.

13. The players divided into two teams.

14. Each of the teams defended a basket.

15. For a score a player would throw the ball into the opposite basket.

CHAPTER 7 **Phrases** *(pages 44–49)*

Finding Appositives and Appositive Phrases

An **appositive** is a noun or pronoun that identifies or explains another noun or pronoun in the sentence.

◆ Underline each appositive or appositive phrase.

1. Mr. Rich, our football coach, is looking forward to a great season this year.

2. Todd, the team captain, has been working hard all summer.

3. Tomorrow is the game against our rival school Central.

4. The referee, the one with the black hat, gave our team a penalty.

5. The song "Fire Away" will be our fight song this year.

6. The coach called for a new play, Blue 42.

7. Our receiver, the one with the school record, caught the pass in the end zone.

8. Billy, our kicker, scored the winning point.

9. Mrs. Johnson, the journalism teacher, said we should interview Billy.

10. Arthur Donovan, the opposing coach, congratulated our school.

CHAPTER 7   **Phrases**   *(pages 44–49)*

Punctuating Sentences with Appositives or Appositive Phrases

◆ Add or delete commas so they are used correctly with appositives or appositive phrases in the sentences below. If a sentence is correct, make no changes.

1. My brother, Bob, likes to read.

2. The book, *The Adventures of Tom Sawyer*, is one of his favorites.

3. *The Adventures of Huckleberry Finn* a book by Mark Twain is also a favorite.

4. Tom my younger brother enjoys building models with his friends.

5. His favorite model, the *Titanic*, is on display in his room.

CHAPTER 7 · Phrases (pages 44–49)

Mixed Practice: Appositive Phrases

◆ Underline each appositive or appositive phrase. Then draw an arrow to the word it identifies or explains.

1. William Sydney Porter, a writer, lived in Austin, Texas.

2. He is known to most people by his pseudonym, O. Henry.

3. O. Henry, a gifted storyteller, impressed many types of people.

4. In 1894, he started a comic magazine, *The Rolling Stone.*

5. The magazine, a humorous weekly, failed after a few issues.

6. After he moved to Houston, Porter took a job as a journalist on the local paper, *The Post.*

7. O. Henry, a talented writer, published many different types of short stories.

8. His most famous collection, *The Four Million*, appeared in 1906.

9. This collection includes one of his best stories, "The Gift of the Magi."

10. The story, a tale of sacrifice and irony, takes place at Christmas.

11. Another short story, "The Ransom of Red Chief," takes place in the Old South.

12. Two characters, Bill Driscoll and the storyteller, decide to kidnap the only child of a prominent citizen.

13. The child, Red Chief, is so wild that the kidnappers pay his father to take him back!

14. The collection *Heart of the West* contains stories set mostly in Texas.

15. Little is known about the personal life of O. Henry, a very private man.

CHAPTER 8   **Verbals and Verbal Phrases**   *(pages 50–57)*

Finding Participles

A **participle** is a verb form that is used as an adjective.

◆ <u>Underline</u> each participle.

1. The scientists could hear the howling coyotes.

2. The coyote's expanding range presents a challenge for scientists.

3. A coyote can live anywhere from the frozen mountains to the hot deserts.

4. A starving coyote will scavenge in trash cans.

5. A coyote will change its breeding habits for adaptation.

6. Controlled hunts wiped out the coyote population in central Texas and much of North Dakota.

7. Lost pets often become prey for coyotes.

8. A hunting coyote will stalk its prey patiently.

9. Exhausted animals are no match for the coyote's stamina.

10. The coyote is a protected species in only twelve states.

CHAPTER 8 · Verbals and Verbal Phrases *(pages 50–57)*

Finding the Words Participles Modify

◆ <u>Underline</u> each participle. Then draw an arrow to the word each participle modifies.

1. A determined schoolteacher made an unusual bicycle trip.

2. Byron Vouga has no functioning kidneys.

3. Two failed transplants resulted in dialysis three times a week.

4. The courageous Vouga planned an exhausting cross-country bicycle trip.

5. Vouga endured blistering heat and many other trials as a fund-raiser for the fight against kidney disease.

6. Scheduled stops at clinics for Vouga's dialysis were part of the trip.

7. Vouga met many unrecognized heroes who live with kidney disease every day.

8. One person has been on dialysis for twenty years and still works at a towing service.

9. Byron Vouga is truly an amazing man and an inspiration to others.

10. His challenging task brings hope to many people with kidney disease.

CHAPTER 8   Verbals and Verbal Phrases   *(pages 50–57)*

Participle or Verb?

◆ Label each underlined word *P* for participle or *V* for verb.

1. The <u>dancing</u> children delighted the audience.

2. Marcie had <u>spoken</u> to the audience about the show.

3. Clap your hands with the <u>syncopated</u> rhythm.

4. The singers were <u>standing</u> under the bright lights.

5. By the end of the show, everyone was <u>singing</u>!

6. We gave the actors a <u>standing</u> ovation.

7. Everyone was <u>dancing</u> in the aisles.

8. Beth's <u>spoken</u> monologue went well.

9. Mrs. Owen <u>syncopated</u> the soprano part.

10. The <u>singing</u> dog was a great addition to the show.

CHAPTER 8   Verbals and Verbal Phrases   *(pages 50–57)*

Finding Participial Phrases

◆ <u>Underline</u> each participial phrase.

1. Pushing deep into the land to the northwest, Lewis and Clark hoped for a route to the Pacific.

2. The Corps of Discovery, chosen carefully by Lewis and Clark, explored the Louisiana Territory.

3. Born around 1787, Sacajawea did not join the Lewis and Clark expedition until 1805.

4. Sacajawea, known also as Bird Woman, served as an interpreter and guide for the expedition.

5. Taken captive as a child, she had grown up in a Hidatsa village far from her Shoshone people.

6. Knowing that Sacajawea was a Shoshone, the explorers wanted her help.

7. The Rocky Mountains, looming ahead, provided a natural rest stop.

8. Needing horses, Lewis and Clark stopped at a nearby Shoshone village.

9. Immediately Sacajawea recognized several Shoshone mounted on horses.

10. Weeping with joy, Sacajawea was reunited with her people.

11. Sacajawea, serving as an interpreter, helped Lewis and Clark buy several horses.

12. Riding Shoshone horses over the mountains, the explorers pushed onward.

CHAPTER 8   Verbals and Verbal Phrases   *(pages 50–57)*

Recognizing Participial Phrases as Modifiers

◆ <u>Underline</u> each participial phrase. Then draw an arrow to the word each phrase modifies.

1. Viewed through a telescope, Saturn is one of the most unusual objects in the sky.

2. Saturn, named for an ancient Roman god, is yellow and gray.

3. Known as the ringed planet, Saturn is easily recognized.

4. Saturn is one of the giant outer planets characterized by large size and low density.

5. Composed mostly of hydrogen and helium, Saturn's atmosphere is not fit for human life.

6. Saturn's rings, first seen by Galileo in 1610, make it a unique planet.

7. Looking through a telescope, you can see six of Saturn's twenty satellites.

8. The largest satellite rotating around Saturn is called Titan.

9. Titan's diameter is about 3,200 miles, measuring larger than Mercury and Pluto.

10. Discovered in 1655, Titan has a substantial atmosphere.

11. Hidden by its thick atmosphere, the surface of the satellite is not easily seen.

12. The atmosphere of Titan, consisting chiefly of nitrogen, cannot support the life forms of the earth.

CHAPTER 8 **Verbals and Verbal Phrases** *(pages 50–57)*

Writing Sentences with Participial Phrases

◆ Write original sentences using the following participial phrases.

◆ gazing at the night sky

1. _____

_____

◆ known for its brightness

2. _____

_____

◆ revolving around the planet

3. _____

_____

◆ seen from Earth

4. _____

_____

◆ sighted in the eastern sky

5. _____

_____

◆ shining under the stars

6. _____

_____

CHAPTER 8   Verbals and Verbal Phrases   *(pages 50–57)*

Punctuating Participial Phrases

◆ Add or delete commas to make the participial phrases in the sentences below correct. If a sentence is correct, make no changes.

1. Wandering through the planetarium, we learned many amazing facts about the beautiful night sky.

2. Tom reading from one of the displays learned about stars and sailors.

3. Ancient sailors navigating without fancy instruments used the stars for guidance across the ocean.

4. Ancient navigators were also helped by the full moon shining above.

5. Shaking his head in amazement Mr. Guerrero said that ancient people must have been brave.

CHAPTER 8   Verbals and Verbal Phrases   *(pages 50–57)*

Finding Participial Phrases

◆ Write *C* in the blank for each participial phrase that is placed correctly and *I* for each participial phrase that is placed incorrectly.

_____ 1. Maria and Keisha watched a camel waiting for their popcorn.

_____ 2. Tanya, tired from the long walk on the trail, noticed a bobcat.

_____ 3. Singing clearly and loudly, Rico heard the rare bird.

_____ 4. Shawna took a picture of a lion panting in the hot sun.

_____ 5. Walking through the city zoo, Chen saw a ferocious tiger.

_____ 6. Tony enjoyed the seal swimming in its pool.

_____ 7. Morgan watched a raccoon talking quietly with her friends.

_____ 8. Swinging from the trees, the children laughed at the chimpanzee.

_____ 9. The elephants eyed the children spraying water from their trunks.

_____ 10. A giraffe, chewing on some leaves, cautiously watched Nita.

CHAPTER 8 Verbals and Verbal Phrases   *(pages 50–57)*

Correcting Misplaced Participial Phrases

◆ Rewrite the incorrect sentences from the preceding exercise. Move the phrases so that the sentences make sense.

1. _____

_____

2. _____

_____

3. _____

_____

4. _____

_____

5. _____

_____

CHAPTER 8 Verbals and Verbal Phrases *(pages 50–57)*

Recognizing Infinitives

An **infinitive** is a verb form that usually begins with *to*. It is used as a noun, an adjective, or an adverb.

◆ Underline each infinitive.

1. Kathy really likes to shop.

2. The best mall to visit is the Northgate Mall.

3. I visited the mall only to look.

4. To shop isn't the only reason for visiting the mall.

5. Danny likes to eat.

6. Which is the best restaurant to try?

7. My mom will go with us to supervise.

8. Do you know which way to go?

9. Is Jill's mother going to drive?

10. My mom likes to browse.

CHAPTER 8   Verbals and Verbal Phrases   *(pages 50–57)*

Infinitive or Prepositional Phrase?

◆ Label each underlined phrase *I* for infinitive or *PP* for prepositional phrase.

1. There are many different factors that contribute <u>to research</u>.

2. It is important <u>to plan</u> your research paper very carefully.

3. Once you have completely developed your plan, get <u>to work</u>.

4. <u>To research</u> for any topic will require some supplies.

5. Organize all of your research information according <u>to type</u>.

6. You should plan <u>to school</u> yourself thoroughly in your topic.

7. If you follow a schedule, your research should proceed according <u>to plan</u>.

8. Several people went <u>to school</u> and wrote their papers in the computer lab.

9. It is difficult <u>to work</u> when it is noisy in the room.

10. If your final draft is long, you will need lots of patience <u>to type</u> it.

CHAPTER 8   Verbals and Verbal Phrases   *(pages 50–57)*

Finding Infinitive Phrases

An **infinitive phrase** is an infinitive with its modifiers and complements—all working together as a noun, adjective, or an adverb.

◆ <u>Underline</u> each infinitive phrase.

1. Two-year-old Bonnie Blair learned to skate from her siblings.

2. They did not want Bonnie to use double runners on her skates.

3. Double runners make it easier for a child to stand up on skates.

4. Bonnie quickly learned to take a few steps on the skates.

5. She always wanted to skate in the Olympics.

6. Bonnie, a good student, was allowed to graduate from high school early.

7. A group of police officers decided to help Bonnie.

8. They raised $7,000 to pay for her Olympic training costs.

9. Bonnie knows what it is like to win at the Olympics.

10. She has many gold medals to prove her ability.

11. Samuel Clemens was apprenticed to work as a printer.

12. Instead he became a journalist and began to write for a living.

13. He decided to use the pen name Mark Twain.

14. Rivermen used the call "mark twain" to mark the depth of the river.

15. In 1871, he quit journalism to devote his full attention to literature.

CHAPTER 8 **Verbals and Verbal Phrases** *(pages 50–57)*

Writing Sentences with Infinitive Phrases

◆ Write five sentences, using the following infinitive phrases.

◆ to read a good book

1. _____

_____

◆ to study hard

2. _____

_____

◆ to copy in my notebook

3. _____

_____

◆ to photograph the scene

4. _____

_____

◆ to research the topic well

5. _____

_____

CHAPTER 8 • Verbals and Verbal Phrases *(pages 50–57)*

Mixed Practice: Verbals and Verbal Phrases

◆ <u>Underline</u> each verbal or verbal phrase. Then label each one *P* for participle, *PP* for participial phrase, *I* for infinitive, or *IP* for infinitive phrase.

1. Searching the ocean floor carefully, treasure hunters look for remains of old ships.

2. Stolen treasure is rumored to be near the town of Wellfleet, Massachusetts.

3. Barry Clifford hopes to find the remains of the pirate ship *Whydah*.

4. The *Whydah*, laden with heavy treasure, sank in a storm on April 26, 1717.

5. The storm caused the ship to break apart.

6. To aid Clifford in his search, several experts have signed on his workboat *Vast Explorer II.*

7. The best artifact to find is the hull with the treasures of the ship.

8. A smiling diver emerges with black disks in his hands.

9. The diver floating in the water has found some coins.

10. He boards the research vessel to show them to an eager crew.

CHAPTER 9 **Clauses** *(pages 58–67)*

Independent or Subordinate Clause?

A **clause** is a group of words that has a subject and a verb.

An **independent, or main, clause** can stand alone as a sentence because it expresses a complete idea.

A **subordinate, or dependent, clause** cannot stand alone as a sentence because it does not express a complete thought.

◆ Label each underlined clause *I* for independent or *S* for subordinate.

_____ 1. <u>If the sky is dark and cloudy,</u> you should bring an umbrella.

_____ 2. <u>Unless you call first,</u> I will leave for the beach at noon.

_____ 3. <u>I like this beach</u> because it is almost never crowded.

_____ 4. Since the tide is in, <u>the water is high.</u>

_____ 5. We will eat <u>when Terry and Yolanda finally get here.</u>

_____ 6. <u>Before the rain started,</u> we played a game of volleyball.

_____ 8. <u>Sometimes we surf</u> while we are at the beach with our friends.

_____ 9. I watched television <u>after I got home from the beach.</u>

_____ 10. <u>Someone knocked on the door</u> as soon as I got home.

Name _____ Date _____

CHAPTER 9   **Clauses**   *(pages 58–67)*

....

Supplying Subordinating Conjunctions

An **adverb clause** is a subordinate clause that is used mainly to modify a verb.

◆ Rewrite each sentence, replacing the blank with a subordinate conjunction to create a subordinate clause.

1. ___ the bald eagle is our national bird, it is protected from hunters.

   _____

   _____

2. ___ the bald eagle has been our national symbol since 1782, many people want to protect it.

   _____

   _____

3. ___ pesticides were used, many eagles died in the 1970s.

   _____

   _____

4. ___ the bald eagle became an endangered species, scientists studied it carefully.

   _____

   _____

5. It proved to be a relatively easy task ___ eagles reuse the same nest sites.

   _____

   _____

6. Eagles are convenient to study ___ several pairs of eagles nest in a small area.

   _____

   _____

CHAPTER 9 **Clauses** *(pages 58–67)*

Finding Adverb Clauses

◆ Underline the adverb clause in each sentence. Then draw an arrow to the word or words that the adverb clause modifies.

1. Although Detroit is called "the Motor City," its football team is named after an animal.

2. Because George Richards owned a radio station, the team's owner held a contest to name the new football team.

3. The team became the Detroit Lions after the contest had ended.

4. When the team won many games the first season, fans cheered.

5. After the Lions won the Western Division title in 1935, they advanced to the championship.

6. New York fans were disappointed when the Lions beat the Giants.

7. As soon as the game was over, Detroit celebrated.

8. Though they had won the championship in 1935, Detroit was 7–3 in 1936.

9. It would be several seasons before the Lions had another championship.

10. Until the team acquired some new players, winning seasons would be scarce.

Name _____ Date _____

Writing Sentences with Adverb Clauses

◆ Write five original sentences, using the following adverb clauses. Be sure you use commas correctly.

◆ because football is so popular

1. _____

_____

◆ as soon as the game starts

2. _____

_____

◆ after we scored the winning touchdown

3. _____

_____

◆ since we will go to the state championship this year

4. _____

_____

◆ before we go to the playoffs

5. _____

_____

CHAPTER 9 **Clauses** *(pages 58–67)*

Punctuating Sentences with Adverb Clauses

◆ Add or remove commas where needed in the following sentences. If a sentence is correct, make no changes.

1. Whenever I watch football I like to cheer for my team.

2. While the game is on, you shouldn't talk to my dad.

3. As soon as it's halftime we will get a pretzel at the snack bar.

4. Unless they want to repeat last year's performance our team should spend more time on fundamentals.

5. We should get our tickets before the game is sold out.

CHAPTER 9   **Clauses**   *(pages 58–67)*

Finding Adjective Clauses

An **adjective clause** is a subordinate clause that is used to modify a noun or a pronoun.

◆ <u>Underline</u> each adjective clause.

1. King Arthur, who is the subject of many legends, may have been a real person.

2. There are few stories that are like Arthur's.

3. The Dark Ages, which were perhaps the times in which Arthur lived, were very chaotic.

4. Arthur, whose leadership skills were great, united the British people against the Saxon raiders.

5. Arthur's rule was one that would not soon be forgotten.

6. Sir Thomas Malory, who lived during the Middle Ages, wrote about King Arthur.

7. His book, which details the adventures of Arthur's knights, exaggerates some of the stories.

8. Lancelot, who was portrayed as Arthur's best knight, may not have been from France.

9. Merlin, who was believed to be a wizard, was probably just Arthur's adviser.

10. In any case it is a story that intrigues many readers.

CHAPTER 9　Clauses　(pages 58–67)

Identifying the Words that Adjective Clauses Modify

◆ <u>Underline</u> each adjective clause. Then draw an arrow to the word or words that each adjective clause modifies.

1. Joan, who is reading a book about Robin Hood, enjoys legends.

2. It was her love of old legends that interested me in the King Arthur stories.

3. Marco, whose report about the Dark Ages was excellent, wants to write his own book about King Arthur.

4. Missy's report, which was about castles, contained many details.

5. The report that Mrs. Johns liked the best was about ancient legends.

6. Mrs. Johns, who reads widely about historical people and events, learned something new about the Dark Ages from Sue's report.

7. Rahul, who wants to be an archaeologist, wrote about the search for Camelot.

8. The ancient castle, which has never been found, might be fictitious.

9. Jonathan, whose paper was written on the bus, did not hope for a good grade.

10. The paper, which had not been well researched, needed more work, additional information, and a great deal more thought.

CHAPTER 9 **Clauses** *(pages 58–67)*

Writing Sentences with Adjective Clauses

◆ Write five original sentences, using the following adjective clauses. Be sure to use commas correctly.

◆ that I like

1. _____

_____

◆ who is sitting beside me

2. _____

_____

◆ whom I know to be an expert

3. _____

_____

◆ which is her nickname

4. _____

_____

◆ whose computer is broken

5. _____

_____

CHAPTER 9   Clauses   (pages 58–67)

Punctuating Sentences with Adjective Clauses

◆ Add or remove commas where needed in the following sentences. If a sentence is correct, make no changes.

1. Our school library which is huge is a good place for research.

2. Mrs. Engel, who is our librarian, is a wonderful resource person.

3. The place in the library that I like best is the technology room.

4. Jim whose knowledge of computers is amazing is a good friend to take to the library.

5. Mrs. Engel whom I respect highly always finds the right book for me.

CHAPTER 9 **Clauses** *(pages 58–67)*

Mixed Practice: Adverb and Adjective Clauses

◆ Label each underlined clause *ADV* for adverb or *ADJ* for adjective.

1. <u>Although he had been diagnosed with cancer in 1996</u>, Lance Armstrong overcame the disease.

2. Lance Armstrong, <u>who looks to his mother for inspiration</u>, trained hard for the 1999 Tour de France.

3. Armstrong was not discouraged <u>though doctors had given him only a 50–50 chance for recovery</u>.

4. <u>When Armstrong crossed the finish line at the end of the race</u>, he had accomplished the impossible.

5. The Tour de France, <u>which is a cycling event</u>, takes place every year in July.

6. <u>Even though Armstrong was in good physical condition</u>, doctors credit his recovery to his positive attitude.

7. Armstrong says, "<u>If you ever get a second chance in life</u>, you've got to go all the way."

8. Lance Armstrong, <u>who held a commanding lead after three stages of the event</u>, rode hard every day.

9. <u>As soon as he crossed the finish line</u>, a great cheer went up.

10. Many Americans, <u>who interrupted their vacations</u>, congratulated Lance Armstrong, the winner.

CHAPTER 9   Clauses   *(pages 58–67)*

Recognizing Misplaced Adjective Clauses

◆ Write *C* in the blank if an adjective clause is placed correctly and *I* if an adjective clause is placed incorrectly.

_____ 1. Bethany, who had a bag of bread crumbs, watched a pigeon.

_____ 2. A goose that had a bump on its head lunged for the bag.

_____ 3. David threw some crumbs to a duck who enjoys feeding the birds.

_____ 4. A grackle that was flying overhead wanted some food.

_____ 5. A dog that had no collar chased some of the ducks.

_____ 6. My sister that had been abandoned observed a nest.

_____ 7. Koreen threw some crumbs to the swans who had an extra bag.

_____ 8. A turtle that was eager to investigate climbed to the shore.

_____ 9. Marta explored the pool whose love of wildlife is well known.

_____ 10. Deb saw a duck who never really wanted to come along.

_____ 11. The duck, which was following its mother, lagged behind.

_____ 12. People waited in line who wanted to ride the paddleboats.

_____ 13. The line, which curved around several times, was very long.

_____ 14. Stephen, who was holding his brother's hand, became impatient.

_____ 15. He picked up some tiny pebbles and threw them into the water that were on the ground.

Name _____ Date _____

CHAPTER 9   **Clauses**   *(pages 58–67)*

Correcting Sentences with Misplaced Adjective Clauses

◆ Rewrite the incorrect sentences from the preceding exercise, placing the adjective clauses properly. Be sure to use commas where needed.

1. _____

_____

2. _____

_____

3. _____

_____

4. _____

_____

5. _____

_____

6. _____

_____

7. _____

_____

CHAPTER 9 **Clauses** *(pages 58–67)*

Recognizing Simple and Compound Sentences

A **simple sentence** is a sentence that has one subject and one verb.

A **compound sentence** is made up of two or more simple sentences, usually joined by a comma and a coordinating conjunction: *and, but, or,* or *yet.*

◆ Label each sentence *S* for simple or *C* for compound.

_____ 1. Softball began in Chicago in 1887.

_____ 2. Softball fields require less space than baseball fields.

_____ 3. A game of softball is similar to a game of baseball, but the bases on a softball field are closer together.

_____ 4. Softball bases are sixty feet apart, but baseball requires ninety feet between bases.

_____ 5. A softball pitcher stands 40 to 46 feet from home plate, but the distance in baseball is 60.5 feet.

_____ 6. The circumference of a softball usually measures twelve inches and is larger than a baseball's circumference.

_____ 7. A baseball is about nine inches in circumference.

_____ 8. Baseball players usually leave the base before a pitch, but softball players always wait for a pitch.

_____ 9. Baseball allows a choice of pitches, but softball pitchers always throw underhand.

_____ 10. A softball team has nine or ten players and plays only seven innings.

CHAPTER 9   **Clauses**   *(pages 58–67)*

Simple or Compound Sentence?

◆ Label each sentence *S* for simple or *C* for compound.

_____   1. Yogurt is a good source of calcium, and cheese contains calcium, too.

_____   2. On advice from the Indians, the Pilgrims planted corn and found many uses
              for it.

_____   3. Potato leaves are definitely poisonous, but the potato itself is not.

_____   4. Spinach is a good source of iron and other minerals and can be eaten raw.

_____   5. Three types of roots are onions, turnips, and parsnips.

_____   6. Tomatoes are categorized as fruits, but many people think of tomatoes as
              vegetables.

_____   7. Trout is a very nutritious fish; it contains many nutrients.

_____   8. Raw carrots are crunchy, tasty, and good for you, too.

_____   9. Ice cream contains vitamin D but has a great deal of fat.

_____   10. Chocolate may be junk food, but it tastes good to most people.

Name _____ Date _____

Writing Compound Sentences

◆ Use the following independent clauses to form five compound sentences.

◆ the hamburgers smell delicious

1. _____

_____

◆ they are still pink

2. _____

_____

◆ the picnic starts at one o'clock

3. _____

_____

◆ I don't have a ride

4. _____

_____

◆ Tom made a pie

5. _____

_____

CHAPTER 9   Clauses   (pages 58–67)

Punctuating Compound Sentences

◆ Rewrite the following compound sentences. Be sure that commas, conjunctions, and semicolons are used properly. If a sentence is punctuated correctly, make no changes.

1. Jennifer wanted to have watermelons at the picnic; but they weren't in season.

   _____

   _____

2. Ashley made a chocolate cake but she left it at home.

   _____

   _____

3. Brian cooked the hot dogs he burned only a few.

   _____

   _____

4. Bob wanted to bring cantaloupe yet he couldn't find any.

   _____

   _____

5. Michael made brownies; they were delicious.

   _____

   _____

CHAPTER 9 Clauses *(pages 58–67)*

Distinguishing Among Simple, Compound, and Complex Sentences

A **complex sentence** consists of one independent clause and one or more subordinate clauses.

◆ Label each sentence *S* for simple, *CD* for compound, or *CX* for complex.

_____ 1. Many people associate Benjamin Franklin only with the discovery of electricity, but he had many other notable accomplishments as well.

_____ 2. Although he had only two years of formal schooling, Franklin was an avid reader.

_____ 3. Franklin found a job as a printer, and he began to publish *Poor Richard's Almanac*.

_____ 4. His business expanded further when he did government printing.

_____ 5. He also operated a bookshop, and he became a clerk of the Pennsylvania Assembly.

_____ 6. Franklin, who served as postmaster of Philadelphia, retired at the age of forty-two.

_____ 7. Franklin began yet another career in 1740 when he invented the Franklin stove.

_____ 8. He also read papers about electricity and began a series of experiments.

_____ 9. Franklin became famous when the Royal Society in London published his discoveries.

_____ 10. Benjamin Franklin was a man of many talents, yet few people recognize the breadth of his achievements.

_____ 11. There have been postage stamps in Franklin's honor, and his face is on some currency.

_____ 12. The Franklin Institute in Philadelphia is named for him.

CHAPTER 9 **Clauses** *(pages 58–67)*

Punctuating Complex Sentences

◆ Rewrite the following sentences, adding commas where needed. If a sentence is correct, make no changes.

1. As Franklin traveled throughout the colonies he reorganized the American postal system.

   _____

   _____

2. In October 1776, Franklin sailed for France, where he gained French aid.

   _____

   _____

3. Though he was nearly eighty years old Benjamin Franklin became the first United States government minister to France.

   _____

   _____

4. Franklin outfitted John Paul Jones who owned the ship the *Bonhomme Richard.*

   _____

   _____

5. When Franklin returned home in 1785 he accepted his election as president of the Pennsylvania Executive Council.

   _____

   _____

CHAPTER 9   Clauses   *(pages 58–67)*

Mixed Practice: Kinds of Sentences

◆ Label each sentence *S* for simple, *CD* for compound, or *CX* for complex.

_____   1. Hans Christian Andersen was born in 1805 and died almost seventy years later.

_____   2. He wrote 156 fairy tales, but his most famous tale was "The Ugly Duckling."

_____   3. Andersen grew up in Denmark and lived in a one-room house.

_____   4. Although his father was a shoemaker, he could not afford leather shoes for his own children.

_____   5. Andersen was tall and lanky, and his hands and feet were large.

_____   6. His eyes were small and very close together, and his nose was too big for his face.

_____   7. People made jokes about him or ignored him.

_____   8. As he played by himself, he carved a tiny theater.

_____   9. He made up short plays and acted out all the parts.

_____ 10. After he saw a real play at the age of seven, he longed for the stage.

_____ 11. Later he went to Copenhagen, but no theater there would hire him.

_____ 12. When he wasn't successful, Andersen went back to school and earned good grades.

_____ 13. When he wrote his first fairy tale at the age of thirty, he never expected success.

_____ 14. People all over the world loved his stories, and they still read them today.

CHAPTER 10 Sentence Fragments and Run-ons *(pages 68–71)*

Identifying Sentence Fragments

A **sentence fragment** is a group of words that does not express a complete thought.

◆ Label each group of words *S* for a sentence or *F* for a sentence fragment.

_____ 1. No one thought the Beatles had much talent in the early 1960s.

_____ 2. Said they were a musical disaster.

_____ 3. The band began its career in England.

_____ 4. Their unusual style.

_____ 5. The Beatles' arrival in America.

_____ 6. Their appearance on "The Ed Sullivan Show" was one of the highest-rated programs of its day.

_____ 7. Their music was a hit.

_____ 8. Thousands of fans.

_____ 9. Sold 2.5 million albums and singles in four weeks' time.

_____ 10. The fans went crazy.

_____ 11. Dozens of girls fainted at the Beatles' appearances across America.

_____ 12. The Beatles were the first rock and roll band to play at Carnegie Hall.

_____ 13. Had an amazing tour across most of the United States.

_____ 14. Apparently the critics were wrong.

_____ 15. Changed rock and roll music forever.

CHAPTER 10 **Sentence Fragments and Run-ons** *(pages 68–71)*

Correcting Sentence Fragments

◆ Choose five of the sentence fragments from the preceding exercise to rewrite as complete sentences.

1. _____

_____

2. _____

_____

3. _____

_____

4. _____

_____

5. _____

_____

CHAPTER 10 **Sentence Fragments and Run-ons** *(pages 68–71)*

Mixed Practice: Sentence Fragments

◆ Write *S* if the fragment is missing a subject or *V* if the fragment is missing a verb.

_____ 1. The reed for the clarinet.

_____ 2. Dropped the case on the ground.

_____ 3. Had sprung open.

_____ 4. My new clarinet.

_____ 5. Picked it up and tried the mouthpiece.

_____ 6. A crack on the mouthpiece.

_____ 7. Told my band teacher.

_____ 8. My mom and dad.

_____ 9. The price for the repairs.

_____ 10. My allowance for the next ten weeks.

_____ 11. Once dropped.

_____ 12. Plays the trumpet.

_____ 13. Practices every day.

_____ 14. My brother.

CHAPTER 10   Sentence Fragments and Run-ons   *(pages 68–71)*

Identifying Phrase Fragments

◆ Label each group of words *S* for sentence or *PF* for phrase fragment.

_____   1. In the garden on a hot day.

_____   2. The cucumber plants are very green this year.

_____   3. Watering the garden with a hose.

_____   4. I saw the birds eating the tomatoes again.

_____   5. To stop them from eating all my plants.

_____   6. I work hard to guard against bugs.

_____   7. For the best gardener in my family.

_____   8. My dad knows how to make plants grow.

_____   9. At the end of a long day.

_____   10. We enjoy fresh vegetables from our garden.

CHAPTER 10   Sentence Fragments and Run-ons   *(pages 68–71)*

Identifying Phrase Fragments

◆ Label each group of words *S* for sentence or *PF* for phrase fragment.

_____ 1. George Washington Carver was a professor of agriculture.

_____ 2. At the Tuskegee Institute.

_____ 3. George Washington Carver was an ecologist.

_____ 4. To teach people about using the soil productively.

_____ 5. Carver spent much of his childhood tending the family vegetable garden.

_____ 6. Collecting new flowers.

_____ 7. As a quiet child.

_____ 8. Soon young Carver was known as the "plant doctor."

_____ 9. To help people take care of the land.

_____ 10. Carver's work resulted in many new uses for the peanut plant.

CHAPTER 10 **Sentence Fragments and Run-ons** *(pages 68–71)*

Correcting Phrase Fragments

◆ Rewrite the phrase fragments from the preceding exercise to make complete sentences.

1. _____

_____

2. _____

_____

3. _____

_____

4. _____

_____

5. _____

_____

CHAPTER 10 Sentence Fragments and Run-ons *(pages 68–71)*

Recognizing Clause Fragments

◆ Label each group of words *S* for sentence or *CF* for clause fragment.

_____ 1. Since it is called a wild dog.

_____ 2. Wild dogs are not house pets gone bad.

_____ 3. Tim McNutt spent many years researching African wild dogs.

_____ 4. Who is a wildlife biologist.

_____ 5. Wild dogs are most like wolves.

_____ 6. Which are nearly as endangered as the black rhino.

_____ 7. People mistakenly believe that wild dogs are bad animals.

_____ 8. Although they live in a pack.

_____ 9. Wild dogs sometimes make kills by themselves.

_____ 10. Because they have a tightly structured social system.

CHAPTER 10 Sentence Fragments and Run-ons *(pages 68–71)*

Recognizing Clause Fragments

◆ Label each group of words *S* for sentence or *CF* for clause fragment.

_____ 1. Jean Craighead George wrote *Julie of the Wolves.*

_____ 2. Since the author studied wolf behavior.

_____ 3. Many people have learned much about wolves.

_____ 4. After they have read *Julie and the Wolves.*

_____ 5. Julie, who is the main character.

_____ 6. She runs away from home.

_____ 7. The setting of the story is not a friendly one.

_____ 8. Which is located in the frozen North.

_____ 9. The wolves find her and save her life.

_____ 10. Before she freezes to death.

CHAPTER 10   Sentence Fragments and Run-ons   (pages 68–71)

Revising Sentence Fragments

◆ Rewrite the clause fragments from the preceding exercise to make complete sentences.

1. _____

_____

2. _____

_____

3. _____

_____

4. _____

_____

5. _____

_____

CHAPTER 10 Sentence Fragments and Run-ons *(pages 68–71)*

Identifying Run-on Sentences

A **run-on sentence** is two or more sentences that are written together and are separated by a comma or no mark of punctuation at all.

◆ Label each group of words *S* for sentence or *RO* for run-on.

_____ 1. Bears climb trees like cats, they sink their claws into the bark.

_____ 2. Birds use their bills for many purposes.

_____ 3. Locusts can travel three hundred miles nonstop their average air speed can reach eight miles per hour.

_____ 4. Some centipedes have 28 legs others have as many as 354 legs.

_____ 5. A trout can live in a lake for as long as four years.

_____ 6. A cheetah can reach speeds of over sixty miles per hour.

_____ 7. Humans are very seldom bitten or attacked by vampire bats these flying mammals do not like human blood.

_____ 8. Lionesses do most of the hunting lions defend the territory.

_____ 9. Cobras prey on other poisonous snakes they subdue them with very strong venom.

_____ 10. Great white sharks are the only sharks that regularly attack mammals.

Name _____ Date _____

Identifying Run-on Sentences

◆ Label each group of words *S* for sentence or *RO* for run-on.

_____ 1. In India, people and elephants compete for resources.

_____ 2. Elephants are enormous animals, they need a large amount of space.

_____ 3. India has a very large population and needs land for farming.

_____ 4. Elephants destroy vegetable crops the farmers become angry.

_____ 5. Game wardens have no choice but to capture such animals.

_____ 6. A captured elephant is transported to a wildlife refuge it gets a second chance.

_____ 7. Conservationists are looking for a better solution to the problem.

_____ 8. Some experts believe that people can learn to live with wild animals.

_____ 9. An elephant often returns to the same grazing area, when people move into these areas elephants become upset.

_____ 10. An angry elephant can cause a lot of damage it is a very big animal.

CHAPTER 10 **Sentence Fragments and Run-ons** *(pages 68–71)*

Correcting Run-on Sentences

◆ Rewrite the run-on sentences from the preceding exercise to make complete sentences.

1. _____

   _____

2. _____

   _____

3. _____

   _____

4. _____

   _____

5. _____

   _____

CHAPTER 10 Sentence Fragments and Run-ons *(pages 68–71)*

Mixed Practice: Sentence Fragments and Run-ons

◆ Rewrite each fragment or run-on sentence to make a correct sentence. Add capital letters, commas, conjunctions, and end marks where needed. If a sentence is correct, make no changes.

1. The first subway in the world opened in London. On January 10, 1863.

   _____

   _____

2. A large trench was dug a pavement was laid over it.

   _____

   _____

3. The trains were powered by steam engines, the smoke from the engines filled the tunnels with terrible fumes.

   _____

   _____

4. Ten feet of water once filled the tunnels the subway shut down briefly.

   _____

   _____

5. About thirty years later, London's first "tube tunnel" was built.

   _____

   _____

CHAPTER 11 **Using Verbs** *(pages 72–87)*

Writing the Principal Parts of Regular Verbs

The **principal parts** of a verb are the present, the present participle, the past, and the past participle.

A **regular verb** forms its past and past participle by adding *–ed* or *–d* to the present.

◆ Write the four principal parts of each of the following regular verbs on the lines below. Use *is* when you write the present participle and *have* when you write the past participle. If you are unsure of the spelling of a verb form, look it up in the dictionary.

1. climb _____

2. drag _____

3. suppose _____

4. paint _____

5. wish _____

6. stop _____

7. use _____

8. earn _____

9. skip _____

10. move _____

CHAPTER 11 **Using Verbs** *(pages 72–87)*

Writing Sentences with Regular Verbs

◆ Write five sentences, using the instructions below. Remember to use a helping verb with the present participle and past participle.

◆ Write a sentence using the present form of *laugh*.

1. _____

_____

◆ Write a sentence using the past form of *cry*.

2. _____

_____

◆ Write a sentence using the present participle form of *play*.

3. _____

_____

◆ Write a sentence using the past participle form of *hope*.

4. _____

_____

◆ Write a sentence using the present participle form of *dream*.

5. _____

_____

CHAPTER 11 **Using Verbs** *(pages 72–87)*

....

Using the Correct Verb Form

An **irregular verb** does not form its past and past participle by adding *–ed* or *–d* to the present.

◆ Label each underlined verb form *P* for past or *PP* for past participle.

1. Yesterday no one in the stadium <u>left</u> before the end of the game.

2. Jimmy's old football uniform has finally <u>burst</u> its seams.

3. Who <u>made</u> the winning touchdown last night?

4. Has everyone <u>brought</u> his playbook to today's practice?

5. Coach has <u>said</u> that many times before.

6. You should have <u>put</u> your uniform in your locker at the end of practice.

7. Coach <u>taught</u> us a new play.

8. I <u>let</u> Joe block for me.

9. Danny <u>brought</u> us each a basket of candy from the cheerleaders.

10. I have <u>made</u> the starting lineup.

CHAPTER 11   **Using Verbs**   *(pages 72–87)*

Correcting Sentences with Irregular Verbs

◆ Rewrite the following sentences, replacing the underlined verb with the correct verb form.

1. John <u>bursted</u> through the other team's weak defense.

   _____

   _____

2. The referee <u>putted</u> the ball on the thirty-five-yard line.

   _____

   _____

3. The coach should have <u>letted</u> me play.

   _____

   _____

4. On his last run, Gary <u>brung</u> our team to within scoring distance.

   _____

   _____

5. Benjamin had <u>catched</u> the football very close to the goal line.

   _____

   _____

6. When we beat Central in the last game, we <u>maked</u> the playoffs.

   _____

   _____

Name _____ Date _____

Determining the Correct Verb Form

◆ Underline the correct verb form for each sentence. Remember that *have, has,* or *had* is used with the past participle.

1. Has anyone (saw, seen) the film clip of Mark McGwire's 70th season home run?

2. McGwire had (broke, broken) the record for the most home runs in a season.

3. By the end of the 1998 baseball season, he had (drove, driven) seventy home runs out of the ballpark.

4. His last home run was a moment that has been (froze, frozen) in time.

5. No one has (stole, stolen) McGwire's special memories of that season.

6. During the following season, McGwire (blew, blowed) his 500th career home run ball out of the park in August.

7. McGwire has (took, taken) his record-breaking feats in stride.

8. McGwire (threw, throwed) himself into playing great baseball.

9. He has (spoke, spoken) to the press about his records.

10. He says that as a child, he never (knew, knowed) that he would have such a great baseball career.

CHAPTER 11 Using Verbs (pages 72–87)

Using the Correct Verb Form

◆ Write the past or the past participle of each verb in parentheses to make the sentence correct. Remember that *have*, *has*, or *had* is used with the past participle.

1. Over the past few years, bears have (drive) people to take extra precautions in national parks.

   _____

2. A grizzly bear (break) the spine of a salmon with a snap of its jaws.

   _____

3. In the past grizzly bears have (choose) to be active at night when humans were near.

   _____

4. Bears in campgrounds (give) many groups of campers a fright.

   _____

5. Some campers have (see) bears climbing into tents in search of food.

   _____

6. The grizzly population has (grow) in mountainous areas.

   _____

7. One bear even (take) some fruit from a basket.

   _____

8. Those bears should have (know) to stay away from the ranger station.

   _____

CHAPTER 11 **Using Verbs** *(pages 72–87)*

Correcting Sentences with Irregular Verbs

◆ Write the following sentences, replacing any incorrect verb with the correct verb form. If a sentence is correct, make no changes.

1. A bear had broke into Grandma's smokehouse.

   _____

   _____

2. Fortunately, the bear choose only the smallest piece of meat.

   _____

   _____

3. Grandma has spoke with the local game warden.

   _____

   _____

4. Last year a bear steal three of Grandma's hams.

   _____

   _____

5. She should have known that bears would want the food.

   _____

   _____

CHAPTER 11 Using Verbs *(pages 72–87)*

....

Determining the Correct Verb Form

◆ <u>Underline</u> the correct verb form for each sentence. Remember that *have, has,* or *had* is used with the past participle.

1. Has Patrick ever (did, done) this kind of rodeo work before?

2. The steer (ran, run) crazily into the center of the ring.

3. Have you ever (went, gone) to a rodeo?

4. I (began, begun) barrel racing when I was seven years old.

5. The starting bell (rang, rung) three minutes ago.

6. Has Nick ever (wore, worn) that blue plaid cowboy shirt?

7. Jessica (drank, drunk) three glasses of water after her barrel race.

8. Do you know who (sang, sung) the national anthem?

9. Have you (wrote, written) a thank-you note to the judging committee?

10. My head (swam, swum) after I tripped and fell in front of the stands.

Name _____ Date _____

Using the Correct Verb Form

◆ Write the past or the past participle of each verb in parentheses to make the sentence correct. Remember that *have, has,* or *had* is used with the past participle.

1. The three tenors (do) a second encore at the end of their performance.

   _____

2. Had those four sopranos ever (sing) together before?

   _____

3. The critics should have (eat) their words about the concert.

   _____

4. The conductor must have (ride) to rehearsal with the drummer, because they were both late.

   _____

5. The singers should have (came) an hour before the show.

   _____

6. Rehearsal had (begin) without the dancers on the stage.

   _____

7. All the musicians (wear) special jackets for the evening's first performance with the tenors.

   _____

8. Who (write) that aria?

   _____

CHAPTER 11 **Using Verbs** *(pages 72–87)*

Finding the Principal Parts in a Dictionary

◆ Use a dictionary to find the principal parts of the following verbs. Then write the present, present participle, past, and past participle of each verb.

1. think _____

2. fly _____

3. raise _____

4. bite _____

5. win _____

6. shake _____

7. lead _____

8. catch _____

9. tear _____

10. spring _____

Name _____ Date _____

Correcting Sentences with Irregular Verbs

◆ Rewrite each of the following sentences, replacing any incorrect verb forms with the correct verb form. If a sentence is correct, make no changes.

1. Shannon sung her first solo at the concert last night.

   _____

   _____

2. The concert almost begun without her and Samantha.

   _____

   _____

3. Shannon had wrote the song especially for her performance.

   _____

   _____

4. Marti did a dance after Shannon's solo.

   _____

   _____

5. Christina's parents come to the concert at intermission.

   _____

   _____

CHAPTER 11 **Using Verbs** *(pages 72–87)*

Mixed Practice: Past and Past Participle

◆ Write the past or the past participle of each verb in parentheses to make the sentences correct.

1. People (write) and (say) why their city should be the nation's capital.

   _____

2. Congress finally (decide) to create a new city.

   _____

3. Congress (pass) a bill in 1790 giving permission to the president to choose a site.

   _____

4. George Washington (go) to several places and (choose) the place where the city now stands.

   _____

5. He (know) it was a good location because the Potomac River (run) deep enough for ships.

   _____

6. Maryland and Virginia (give) the land to the federal government.

   _____

7. President Washington then (bring) in a French architect to design the new city.

   _____

8. The architect (begin) to draw plans with broad avenues.

   _____

CHAPTER 11   Using Verbs   *(pages 72–87)*

Using *Bring* and *Take* Correctly

◆ Read these sentences aloud to practice using the correct verb form.

1. What are you taking to Bill's party tomorrow?

2. Sue brought me a pie for dessert.

3. Bring your CD player to my house before the party.

4. Joe took a ladder to Bill's house to help with the decorations.

5. Denise is bringing her volleyball net here.

◆ <u>Underline</u> the correct form of *bring* or *take*.

6. Wolf pups wait for their mother to (bring, take) them food.

7. The pups (bring, take) food from the adult wolf.

8. The pups (bring, take) the food to a corner and examine it.

9. An adult wolf (brings, takes) its pups along on hunts when the pups are about six months old.

10. Wolves were (brought, taken) to Yellowstone Park, away from their natural habitat.

Name _____ Date _____

CHAPTER 11　Using Verbs　(pages 72–87)

Using *Learn* and *Teach* Correctly

◆ Read these sentences aloud to practice using the correct verb form.

1. I promise I will learn this movement by Friday.

2. Mrs. Arnold has taught piano for many years.

3. Sarah is learning a new solo for the concert.

4. We learned about Mozart in class today.

5. Mr. Johns taught us many facts about Mozart's music.

◆ Underline the correct form of *learn* or *teach*.

6. Mozart (learned, taught) a great deal about music from his father, Leopold.

7. Before he was six years old, young Wolfgang had (learned, taught) to compose symphonies.

8. Many children have (learned, taught) one of his earliest compositions, "Twinkle, Twinkle, Little Star."

9. Mozart's father had (learned, taught) Wolfgang to play a number of instruments.

10. His music (learns, teaches) people many things about patterns of music.

CHAPTER 11 **Using Verbs** (pages 72–87)

Using *Leave* and *Let* Correctly

◆ Read these sentences aloud to practice using the correct verb form.

1. Let me take your suitcase.

2. I will put it in our car by the curb and leave it there.

3. Mark is letting me take care of his dog while he is away.

4. Denise placed her tickets on the counter and left them there.

5. I have let Kathy use my suitcase for her vacation three times now.

◆ <u>Underline</u> the correct form of *leave* or *let*.

6. Please (leave, let) me drive you to the airport.

7. Has Judy's plane (left, let) yet?

8. Margie had (left, let) yesterday for Denver.

9. I am (leaving, letting) Jane borrow my camera for her trip to Greece.

10. What time does your plane (leave, let) the gate?

CHAPTER 11 **Using Verbs** *(pages 72–87)*

Using Problem Verbs

◆ Rewrite each sentence, replacing the incorrect verb with the correct verb form.

1. Please learn me to read the train schedule.

_____

_____

2. Let your suitcase with the ticket agent.

_____

_____

3. You should bring a jacket on your trip to Denver.

_____

_____

4. I taught to read an airport departure board when I was very young.

_____

_____

5. Kelly left me take her hair dryer on the trip since mine was broken.

_____

_____

Name _____ Date _____

CHAPTER 11 Using Verbs *(pages 72–87)*

Mixed Practice: Verb Forms

◆ Underline the correct form of each verb in parentheses.

1. The Chicago Field Museum (learned, taught) us about a dinosaur fossil.

2. The fossil (brought, took) many scientists to the museum.

3. Scientists have (learned, taught) much about dinosaurs from this fossil.

4. The fossil, named Sue, was (brought, taken) here to Chicago because of the work of a paleontologist named Sue Hendricksen.

5. Once a fossil has been discovered, scientists seldom (leave, let) the site.

6. They hope to (learn, teach) about how the dinosaurs lived.

7. The Chicago Museum hopes to (leave, let) the public view the bones soon.

8. They hope that Sue will (bring, take) many visitors to the museum.

9. The scientists will (leave, let) the excavation site as they found it.

10. Paleontologists have (learned, taught) that dinosaurs suffered from gum disease.

CHAPTER 11 Using Verbs (pages 72–87)

Identifying Verb Tenses

The time expressed by a verb is called the **tense** of the verb.

◆ Label the tense of each underlined verb as present, past, future, present perfect, past perfect, or future perfect.

1. A cheetah <u>becomes</u> an adult when it is only two years old.

2. A mother cheetah <u>has brought</u> her cubs part of a gazelle.

3. In a single day, a mother cheetah <u>has hunted</u> a number of times.

4. A female cheetah <u>will catch</u> live prey for her cubs to practice hunting.

5. The cheetah <u>broke</u> sixty miles per hour during the hunt.

6. After the cheetah <u>had stalked</u> its prey, it burst into a run.

7. Cheetahs <u>live</u> in dry grassland areas of Africa.

8. A cheetah <u>will accelerate</u> to top speed in three seconds.

9. The cheetah <u>has survived</u> in the plains of Africa for thousands of years.

10. The cheetah <u>makes</u> facial expressions with the bold black lines around its muzzle.

CHAPTER 11 Using Verbs *(pages 72–87)*

....

Writing Different Tenses

◆ Write the verbs, following the instructions below.

1. Write the present tense of *call.* _____

2. Write the past tense of *burst.* _____

3. Write the present perfect tense of *say.* _____

4. Write the future tense of *teach.* _____

5. Write the past perfect tense of *stop.* _____

6. Write the future perfect tense of *talk.* _____

Name _____ Date _____

CHAPTER 11 Using Verbs *(pages 72–87)*

....

Changing Tenses of Verbs

◆ Rewrite the following sentences so that each underlined verb is in the past perfect tense.

1. The cheetah <u>survives</u> well in the wild.

   _____

   _____

2. Cheetahs <u>have climbed</u> trees to get a good view of their territory.

   _____

   _____

3. Cheetah cubs <u>have led</u> sheltered lives.

   _____

   _____

4. By the end of the day, cheetah cubs <u>will have played</u> for many hours.

   _____

   _____

5. The cheetah <u>will continue</u> to thrive.

   _____

   _____

CHAPTER 11 **Using Verbs** *(pages 72–87)*

Correcting Shifts in Verb Tense

◆ Write *S* in the blank if a sentence contains a shift in verb tense. If a sentence is correct, write *C*.

_____ 1. Before you leave for the race, check your equipment and gear.

_____ 2. When I checked my bike before the race, I find a flat rear tire.

_____ 3. Because I didn't have a patch kit, I will not ride in the race.

_____ 4. Joe says that he has a patch kit.

_____ 5. I told him that I needed a patch for my flat tire.

_____ 6. Joe gave me the kit, and I fixed the flat tire very quickly.

_____ 7. After I fix the flat tire, I left for the big bicycle race.

_____ 8. The new tire will help my performance and gave me more traction.

◆ Rewrite the sentences in the preceding exercise that contain shifts in verb tense.

1. _____

_____

2. _____

_____

3. _____

_____

4. _____

_____

CHAPTER 11 **Using Verbs** (pages 72–87)

Identifying Progressive Verb Forms

◆ <u>Underline</u> each verb phrase.

1. By today's end, we will have been announcing the Kentucky Derby for twenty-five years.

2. We will be watching the entrance of the horses.

3. The horses have been prancing in anticipation of the race.

4. The favorite has been racing well all season.

5. Last year he had been placing second or third on a regular basis.

6. Today his trainer is hoping for a win.

7. The horses will be entering the post parade in a moment.

8. The gray horse is pawing the ground impatiently.

9. The jockeys are planning their strategies.

10. Earlier the crowd was acting restless.

Name _____ Date _____

Changing Verb Tenses

◆ Rewrite each of the following sentences so that it contains a progressive verb.

1. The greatest names in thoroughbred racing have gathered in Louisville.

   _____

   _____

2. The horses have practiced for weeks.

   _____

   _____

3. The crowd roars.

   _____

   _____

4. The horses enter the starting gate.

   _____

   _____

5. The gates fly open.

   _____

   _____

CHAPTER 11 Using Verbs *(pages 72–87)*

Mixed Practice: Verb Tenses

◆ Write each underlined verb in the tense that is indicated in parentheses.

1. Nile crocodiles <u>live</u> (present perfect progressive) in Africa for many years.

   _____

2. By the time it <u>reach</u> (present) maturity, a crocodile <u>weigh</u> (present) up to 2,220 pounds.

   _____

3. Crocodiles <u>grow</u> (present perfect) to twenty feet.

   _____

4. Some ancient people <u>believe</u> (past) that the crocodile was sly.

   _____

5. Crocodiles <u>continue</u> (future) to thrive because people <u>preserve</u> (future) their habitats.

   _____

6. The crocodile <u>survive</u> (past perfect) due to its toughness.

   _____

7. During the last wet season the crocodiles <u>live</u> (past) in rain puddles.

   _____

8. By midday a crocodile <u>wait</u> (future progressive) patiently for its prey.

   _____

CHAPTER 12 Using Pronouns *(pages 88–101)*

Identifying the Cases of Personal Pronouns

Case is the form of a noun or pronoun that indicates its use in a sentence.

◆ Underline the personal pronouns in each sentence. Label each personal pronoun *N* for nominative, *O* for objective, or *P* for possessive.

1. They are going to the stables.

2. That is he on the tall chestnut horse.

3. I left my saddle in the barn.

4. We like riding through the countryside.

5. That saddle belongs to me.

6. Our riding instructor taught us to groom the horses.

7. My horse kept tossing its head.

8. Justin had trouble with his horse, too.

9. We tried to control our horses, but they wouldn't behave.

10. Please tell me how to keep my horse from stopping suddenly.

CHAPTER 12 Using Pronouns *(pages 88–101)*

Using Pronouns as Subjects

The **nominative case** is used both for subjects and for predicate nominatives.

◆ Read each sentence aloud, trying each pronoun separately. Then read the sentence again, underlining the correct pronoun.

1. Last night Fred and (I, me) studied social studies at the library.

2. The Riveras and (we, us) are going to the library after school today.

3. Are Marya and (he, him) doing a science experiment together?

4. Chuck and (she, her) are working together on their history project.

5. The Roys and (they, them) are taping our presentations.

6. Brendan and (I, me) made a model of the White House.

7. After school Tony and (he, him) went to Mr. Bennett's tutorial.

8. Have Min and (she, her) finished their math project?

9. Ali and (I, me) wrote a speech for our presentation together.

10. My parents and (they, them) will meet us at the local library.

CHAPTER 12 **Using Pronouns** *(pages 88–101)*

Using Pronouns as Subjects

◆ <u>Underline</u> the correct personal pronoun for each sentence.

1. (I, me) enjoyed reading *Born Free* by Joy Adamson.

2. (She, Her) adopted a lion cub.

3. (It, Their) was named Elsa.

4. George was Joy's husband, and (he, him) studied lions.

5. Together (they, them) learned much about these animals.

6. (We, Us) all have benefited from the Adamsons' experience.

7. Although Joy loved Elsa, (she, her) knew that the lion deserved to be free.

8. George and Joy did not want to give Elsa up, but (they, them) did.

9. George and (she, her) taught Elsa to be a wild lion.

10. Joy and (he, him) were very sad when Elsa finally set out on her own.

CHAPTER 12 Using Pronouns (pages 88–101)

Using Pronouns as Predicate Nominatives

◆ Underline the correct personal pronoun for each sentence.

1. The best candidate is (she, her).

2. The two people next to Senator Jensen are Mr. Ricker and (she, her).

3. The election monitors will be the teachers or (we, us).

4. The two candidates were Carlos and (I, me).

5. The winners of the election are Tara and (he, him).

6. The best actor to play Romeo was (he, him).

7. That's (he, him) in the movie with Clare Danes.

8. My two favorite actors are Leonardo DiCaprio and (she, her).

9. That's (I, me) in the picture with the movie star.

10. The winner of the award for best actress will be Whoopi Goldberg or (she, her).

11. The extras in the movie will be the boys from Detroit or (we, us).

12. Was that (she, her) in the hot pink dress at the movie premiere last night?

13. My favorite directors are Steven Spielberg and (he, him).

14. The two stunt doubles were Sidney and (I, me).

15. That was (they, them) in the opening scene.

Name _____ Date _____

Supplying Pronouns in the Nominative Case

◆ Rewrite each sentence with an appropriate pronoun. Do not use *you* or *it*.

1. Sandra and ___ are riding the bus to school this year.

   _____

   _____

2. It's ___ in the front seat.

   _____

   _____

3. On the night before school starts, ___ can never get any sleep.

   _____

   _____

4. Laura and ___ just got new clothes for school.

   _____

   _____

5. When did Wade and ___ leave for school?

   _____

   _____

6. Our car pool drivers will be the Samlers and ___.

   _____

   _____

CHAPTER 12 **Using Pronouns** *(pages 88–101)*

Correcting Nominative Case Errors

◆ If an underlined pronoun is in the wrong case, rewrite the sentence correctly. If it is in the correct case, make no changes.

1. The library aides for our class this year are Grace and <u>her</u>.

   _____

   _____

2. Is that <u>he</u> by the cafeteria?

   _____

   _____

3. The twins and <u>me</u> are making plans for a special treat at lunch.

   _____

   _____

4. Bob and <u>me</u> often like to work on science projects together.

   _____

   _____

5. Rico and <u>her</u> will have the same homeroom teacher this year.

   _____

   _____

6. The teachers and <u>them</u> are looking at the new mural.

   _____

   _____

Name _____ Date _____

Writing Sentences with Nominative Case Pronouns

◆ Write five sentences, following the instructions below.

◆ Use *she* as a subject.

1. _____

_____

◆ Use *Patty and I* as a compound subject.

2. _____

_____

◆ Use *neighbors and I* as a compound subject.

3. _____

_____

◆ Use *they* as a predicate nominative.

4. _____

_____

◆ Use *Ken and he* as a compound predicate nominative.

5. _____

_____

CHAPTER 12 **Using Pronouns** *(pages 88–101)*

Mixed Practice: Personal Pronouns

◆ <u>Underline</u> the correct personal pronoun for each sentence.

1. (We, Us) are reading *Where the Red Fern Grows.*

2. (It, they) was written by Wilson Rawls.

3. I think my favorite writer is (he, him).

4. The main character works hard so that (he, him) can afford to buy some hunting dogs.

5. When the dogs arrive, (they, them) are little pups.

6. The boy and the dogs become friends, and (they, them) have many adventures together.

7. Little Ann is small, but (she, her) can think for herself.

8. I think my favorite dog is (she, her).

9. Old Dan is bigger, but (he, him) gets into trouble.

10. Little Ann and (he, him) have all sorts of adventures hunting together.

CHAPTER 12 Using Pronouns *(pages 88–101)*

Using Pronouns as Direct and Indirect Objects

The **objective case** is used for direct objects, indirect objects, and objects of prepositions.

◆ Read each sentence aloud, trying each pronoun separately. Then read the sentence aloud again, underlining the correct pronoun.

1. Give Mom or (we, us) your suitcase.

2. Grandpa told Pepe and (I, me) stories about his last vacation.

3. Did you see the Wilsons or (they, them) this morning?

4. You should have called (we, us) from the airport.

5. Will you drive Aretha and (I, me) to the train station?

6. Mr. Sims promised Pedro and (I, me) a reduced rate on our tickets.

7. Show Earl and (he, him) the pictures from your trip.

8. Did you find Aaron and (she, her) at the wax museum?

9. The onlookers applauded Betty-Sue and (he, him) at the subway station.

10. Evelyn sent Alma and (they, them) a postcard.

CHAPTER 12 Using Pronouns *(pages 88–101)*

Using Pronouns as Direct and Indirect Objects

◆ <u>Underline</u> the correct personal pronoun for each sentence.

1. Joe told (we, us) the new plays for Saturday's game.

2. Give the equipment manager or (they, them) your uniform.

3. The cheerleaders sent Tom and (he, him) some goody bags before the game.

4. Did you see my neighbors or (they, them) in the stands at the game?

5. The crowd cheered Robert and (he, him) for their great team effort.

6. You should have asked (we, us) for help with the new plays.

7. Did you find Alex and (she, her) after the football game yesterday?

8. Will you throw David and (I, me) a few practice passes now?

9. Show Eddie and (he, him) the videotape from the game.

10. Coach Burns promised Sam and (I, me) jobs as mascots last season.

CHAPTER 12 **Using Pronouns** *(pages 88–101)*

Using Pronouns as Objects of Prepositions

◆ Read each sentence aloud, trying each pronoun separately. Then read the sentence aloud again, <u>underlining</u> the correct pronoun.

1. The party is for Tony and (he, him).

2. Jody will give a party for Glen and (I, me) next month.

3. This present is from Keith and (she, her).

4. The bill for the cake will be paid by the Morrisons and (we, us).

5. Is that orange soda for Barney or (he, him)?

6. Hard workers like (they, them) should be invited.

7. I will share my good party pictures with you and (she, her).

8. Send those clear photographs to the Smiths and (they, them).

9. Who will dance with Sara and (they, them)?

10. This is a photograph of Tony and (we, us).

CHAPTER 12 **Using Pronouns** *(pages 88–101)*

Using Pronouns as Objects of Prepositions

◆ Underline the correct personal pronoun for each sentence.

1. The duet was written for Barry and (she, her).

2. The play will be financed by the Smiths and (we, us).

3. Good singers like (they, them) should audition.

4. I will share my script with you and (she, her).

5. Will someone run lines with Ben and (I, me)?

6. Arthur's musical ability was a surprise to (we, us).

7. The play was directed by Thomas and (he, him).

8. Give these costumes to Billy and (they, them).

9. Is that prop for Will or (he, him)?

10. The play was about (she, her).

CHAPTER 12 **Using Pronouns** *(pages 88–101)*

Supplying Pronouns in the Objective Case

◆ Rewrite each sentence with an appropriate pronoun. Do not use *you* or *it*.

1. Mr. Porter gave Maureen and ___ usher uniforms.

   _____

   _____

2. Has Justin given the scripts to Doyle and ___?

   _____

   _____

3. Will you give Janine and ___ some makeup?

   _____

   _____

4. Leila ran across the stage after Rona and ___.

   _____

   _____

5. The Langs invited Cora and ___ to opening night.

   _____

   _____

6. My sister always beats Carlos and ___ to the theater after school.

   _____

   _____

CHAPTER 12 **Using Pronouns** *(pages 88–101)*

Correcting Objective Case Errors

◆ If an underlined pronoun is in the wrong case, write it correctly. If it is in the correct case, make no changes.

1. Mr. Daniels drove Doris and <u>I</u> to play practice.

_____

_____

2. These are the scripts for the new actors and <u>he</u>.

_____

_____

3. Has Jamie given Douglas and <u>she</u> any lines yet?

_____

_____

4. Please give Amanda and <u>he</u> some advice on learning their lines.

_____

_____

5. One line is enough for Sharon and <u>me</u>.

_____

_____

Name _____ Date _____

Writing Sentences with Objective Case Pronouns

◆ Write five sentences, following the instructions below.

◆ Use *him* as a direct object.

1. _____

_____

◆ Use *James or her* as a compound direct object.

2. _____

_____

◆ Use *us* as an indirect object.

3. _____

_____

◆ Use *Carrie and me* as a compound indirect object.

4. _____

_____

◆ Use *me* as the object of the preposition *about*.

5. _____

_____

Name _____ Date _____

CHAPTER 12 Using Pronouns (pages 88–101)

Mixed Practice: Personal Pronouns

◆ Underline the correct personal pronoun for each sentence.

1. Sheila and (I, me) were given a special classroom job.

2. The teacher gave Sheila and (I, me) a special classroom job.

3. I will share all of my history notes with you and (she, her).

4. Give Melinda and (he, him) some of those large index cards.

5. Joan and (he, him) showed me a good Web site for research.

6. Sam and (I, me) want to go to the library tomorrow.

7. Mrs. Nesbitt told Myrna and (he, him) the good news about the special books.

8. Those science books are reserved for Sandy and (I, me).

9. Carl showed (he, him) how to set up the Internet connection.

10. You should have asked (we, us) for some help with your topic.

11. Dave and (I, me) were promised an extra day for research.

12. (I, me) will teach you the correct form for an outline.

13. Give these encyclopedias to (she, her).

14. Ask Mr. Venegas about (they, them).

15. Mrs. Nesbitt dropped (he, him) a hint about an article for his paper.

Name _____ Date _____

Using Possessive Pronouns

The **possessive case** is used to show ownership or possession.

◆ Read each sentence aloud, trying each pronoun separately. Then read the sentence aloud again, <u>underlining</u> the correct pronoun.

1. Where is (your, yours) dog?

2. (My, Mine) is walking in front of the judges' stand.

3. That dog looks a lot like (her, hers).

4. (Their, Theirs) golden retriever won the dog show last year.

5. The dog with the red collar is (our, ours).

6. Which one is (your, yours)?

7. (Her, Hers) poodle is very well behaved.

8. It looks as if the ribbon will be (their, theirs).

9. I had hoped that (my, mine) dog would get a ribbon this year.

10. (Our, Ours) dog did win the obedience portion of the contest.

CHAPTER 12   Using Pronouns   (pages 88–101)

Using Pronouns in the Possessive Case

◆ <u>Underline</u> the correct personal pronoun for each sentence.

1. Which pair of skates is (your, yours)?

2. I got (my, mine) new skates last week.

3. (Our, Ours) skating instructor is teaching us to spin.

4. Are those skates (her, hers)?

5. (Their, Theirs) class is going to a competition next week.

◆ If an underlined pronoun is incorrect, write it correctly. If it is correct, write *Correct*.

6. I like <u>mine</u> new skating instructor. _____

7. <u>Her</u> suggestions are easy to follow. _____

8. The first class on the ice was <u>our</u>. _____

9. <u>Yours</u> skates were in the locker room. _____

10. The team with the most first-place ribbons is <u>theirs</u>. _____

CHAPTER 12   **Using Pronouns**   *(pages 88–101)*

Contraction or Pronoun?

◆ Read each sentence aloud, trying each word separately. Remember to say the two words that make up a contraction. Then read each sentence again, <u>underlining</u> the correct word.

1. Where is (your, you're) apartment?

2. (Its, It's) going to rain tomorrow, so the picnic will have to be at your place.

3. (Hers, Her's) is the best place for a cookout.

4. (Their, They're) car just drove up to your apartment building.

5. (Your, You're) the perfect person to host this picnic.

6. (Theirs, There's) a surprise waiting for you after the picnic.

7. The watermelon is (ours, our's).

8. We should join them at (their, they're) house.

9. My soda lost (its, it's) fizz by the end of the picnic.

10. (Theirs, There's) is the only sugar-free dessert.

Name _____ Date _____

Writing Sentences with Possessive Pronouns and Contractions

◆ Write sentences, using the following words in each.

◆ mine

1. _____

_____

◆ it's

2. _____

_____

◆ hers

3. _____

_____

◆ they're

4. _____

_____

◆ its

5. _____

_____

◆ our

6. _____

_____

CHAPTER 12 Using Pronouns *(pages 88–101)*

Mixed Practice: Personal Pronouns

◆ <u>Underline</u> the correct personal pronoun for each sentence.

1. Last week (I, me) learned about sharks in science.

2. Sharks make (their, they're) homes in the temperate oceans around the world.

3. Long teeth help the shark capture (it, its) prey.

4. The best-known shark scientists are Dr. Eugenie Clark and (he, him).

5. The shark was swimming toward (they, them).

6. When one diver was bothered by a shark, she gave (it, its) a sharp blow to the head.

7. The surprised shark left (she, her) alone.

8. Most great white sharks are quite large, and (they, them) can weigh as much as 7,000 pounds.

9. Dr. Eugenie Clark and (she, her) will be lecturing at our school next week.

10. We hope she will give (we, us) some new information about sharks.

11. Carl and (she, her) did not know that sharks have boneless skeletons.

12. (Their, Theirs) bodies are sleek.

13. Have Karen and (he, him) seen the shark exhibit at the aquarium?

14. Laurie pointed out the model of the shark to Frank and (I, me).

15. (They're, Their) babies are called pups.

CHAPTER 12 Using Pronouns *(pages 88–101)*

Using *Who* and *Whom* Correctly

◆ <u>Underline</u> the correct word in parentheses for each sentence.

1. (Whose, Who's) is this mystery book?

2. (Who, Whom) is your favorite character in the book?

3. About (who, whom) was the novel written?

4. (Who, Whom) is the author?

5. (Who, Whom) did you believe was really telling the truth?

6. (Whose, Who's) was the best alibi?

7. From (who, whom) did you pick up most of your clues?

8. (Who, Whom) did the detective question about the crime?

9. (Who, Whom) committed the crime?

10. (Whose, Who's) giving the book report on the next mystery story?

Name _____ Date _____

Writing Sentences with Interrogative Pronouns

◆ Write five sentences, following the instructions below.

◆ Use *who* as a subject.

1. _____

_____

◆ Use *whose* as a possessive pronoun.

2. _____

_____

◆ Use *whom* as the object of a preposition.

3. _____

_____

◆ Use *whom* as a direct object.

4. _____

_____

◆ Use *who's* as a subject and verb.

5. _____

_____

CHAPTER 12 **Using Pronouns** *(pages 88–101)*

Making Pronouns and Their Antecedents Agree

A pronoun must agree in number and gender with its antecedent.

◆ Rewrite each sentence with an appropriate pronoun.

1. Janice is going on vacation with ___ best friend.

   _____

   _____

2. Mom and Dad packed ___ bags for the trip.

   _____

   _____

3. Thomas packed ___ suitcase yesterday.

   _____

   _____

4. Susan forgot to pack ___ bathing suit.

   _____

   _____

5. My brothers brought ___ sleeping bags to the car this morning.

   _____

   _____

6. Did the girls bring ___ hair dryers?

   _____

   _____

Name _____ Date _____

Correcting Errors with Pronouns and Their Antecedents

◆ Rewrite the following sentences, making sure each pronoun agrees with its antecedent. If a sentence is correct, make no changes.

1. Michelle found her camera on the sofa.

   _____

   _____

2. Jane finished his hamburger.

   _____

   _____

3. A pigeon flapped her wings and begged for food.

   _____

   _____

4. The boys took his video games on the trip to Alaska.

   _____

   _____

5. The Smiths are sending their children to camp for the summer.

   _____

   _____

CHAPTER 12 **Using Pronouns** *(pages 88–101)*

Making Pronouns and Their Antecedents Agree

◆ Rewrite each sentence with an appropriate personal pronoun.

1. Each of the girls on the track team wore ___ school sweater to the game.

   _____

   _____

2. Only one of the other school teams carried ___ coach off the field.

   _____

   _____

3. Both of my sisters like ___ track coach very much.

   _____

   _____

4. Neither of my brothers remembered ___ equipment for the meet today.

   _____

   _____

5. Several of the shoes in the locker room do not have ___ laces.

   _____

   _____

6. Everyone on the boys' team wore ___ jacket in honor of the victory.

   _____

   _____

CHAPTER 12 **Using Pronouns** *(pages 88–101)*

Correcting Errors with Pronouns and Their Antecedents

◆ Rewrite the following sentences, making sure each pronoun agrees with its antecedent. If a sentence is correct, make no changes.

1. Everybody on the girls' teams tried his best.

   _____

   _____

2. Many of the spectators brought its cameras.

   _____

   _____

3. The city has improved his track fields.

   _____

   _____

4. Did anyone on the boys' team lose his key?

   _____

   _____

5. Each of the team members has their own locker.

   _____

   _____

CHAPTER 12 Using Pronouns (pages 88–101)

Recognizing Unclear or Missing Antecedents

Every personal pronoun should clearly refer to a specific antecedent.

◆ Write *I* in the blank for each antecedent that is unclear or missing and *C* for each antecedent that is used correctly.

_____ 1. Jimmy likes the winter because he can go skiing.

_____ 2. At the end of a long day of skiing, it tastes delicious.

_____ 3. I knew Sally was a good skier, but I had never seen any of her skiing until yesterday.

_____ 4. I like skiing because you get to be outside.

_____ 5. Sue's ankle was swollen, but now it has disappeared.

_____ 6. Mom got a new ski pole so that she can ski better.

_____ 7. I enjoy watching other skiers because you can learn different techniques.

_____ 8. Ken emptied his pockets and let them fall to the floor.

_____ 9. I have never tried a ski jump, but I still enjoy skiing.

_____ 10. I usually go skiing early in the morning because then I have the whole day to ski.

CHAPTER 12 **Using Pronouns** *(pages 88–101)*

Correcting Sentences with Unclear or Missing Antecedents

◆ Rewrite the incorrect sentences from the preceding exercise, making the antecedents clear.

1. _____

   _____

2. _____

   _____

3. _____

   _____

4. _____

   _____

5. _____

   _____

CHAPTER 12 **Using Pronouns** *(pages 88–101)*

Mixed Practice: Pronouns

◆ Rewrite each sentence in which the underlined pronoun is used incorrectly. If the pronoun is correct, make no changes

1. <u>Whom</u> is cooking the dinner tomorrow night?

   _____

   _____

2. Everyone says John is a good cook, but I have never tasted any of <u>it</u>.

   _____

   _____

3. Each of the people in my group will bring <u>our</u> favorite dessert to the dinner.

   _____

   _____

4. From <u>whom</u> did you get this recipe?

   _____

   _____

5. Most of the recipe books in my house do not have <u>its</u> covers.

   _____

   _____

6. Few of the boys want to admit that <u>their</u> cooking skills are good.

   _____

   _____

CHAPTER 13 **Subject & Verb Agreement** *(pages 102–113)*

Determining the Number of Nouns and Pronouns

A verb must agree with its subject in number.

◆ Label each word *S* for singular or *P* for plural.

_____ 1. Ohio

_____ 2. they

_____ 3. glove

_____ 4. flower

_____ 5. test

_____ 6. lamps

_____ 7. she

_____ 8. it

_____ 9. boxes

_____ 10. shoe

_____ 11. we

_____ 12. flags

_____ 13. vases

_____ 14. men

_____ 15. horse

_____ 16. car

CHAPTER 13 Subject & Verb Agreement (pages 102–113)

Determining the Number of Verbs

◆ Label each verb *S* for singular or *P* for plural.

_____ 1. Alvin enjoys

_____ 2. we do

_____ 3. twins have

_____ 4. it is

_____ 5. students play

_____ 6. they drive

_____ 7. he was

_____ 8. pictures are

_____ 9. truck has

_____ 10. Pauline does

CHAPTER 13 **Subject & Verb Agreement** *(pages 102–113)*

Making Subjects and Verbs Agree

A singular subject takes a singular verb.

A plural subject takes a plural verb.

◆ Read the following sentences aloud, trying out both forms of the verb in parentheses. Ask yourself whether the subject is singular or plural. Read each sentence aloud again, <u>underlining</u> the correct verb form.

1. Susan (practices, practice) her new dance routine every day.

2. They (studies, study) ballet on Tuesday nights.

3. Geraldine (stretches, stretch) her legs before she starts to dance.

4. Madame (instructs, instruct) her pupils in the most difficult ballet movements.

5. The girls (performs, perform) for their parents.

6. The dancers (is, are) beautiful in their costumes.

7. The dance school (has, have) almost one hundred pupils.

8. Jenny (do, does) enjoy her dance classes.

9. The students (were, was) at class on time.

10. They (surprises, surprise) their teacher constantly.

CHAPTER 13 **Subject & Verb Agreement** *(pages 102–113)*

Making Subjects and Verbs Agree

◆ Underline each subject <u>once</u> and label it *S* for singular or *P* for plural. Then underline <u>twice</u> the form of the verb in parentheses that agrees with the subject.

1. Brown pelicans (dives, dive) into the ocean for fish.

2. A white pelican (scoops, scoop) fish out of the water just below the surface.

3. Mockingbirds (eats, eat) insects.

4. Owls (flies, fly) almost noiselessly.

5. The short-eared owl (helps, help) control rodents.

6. All birds (has, have) special colors and songs.

7. Male blue jays (is, are) a different color than female blue jays.

8. An average condor (have, has) a wingspan of more than nine feet.

9. A duck's webbed feet (acts, act) as paddles.

10. The trumpeter swan (is, are) the largest of all water birds.

CHAPTER 13 **Subject & Verb Agreement** *(pages 102–113)*

Correcting for Subject and Verb Agreement

◆ For each sentence in which the subject and verb do not agree, rewrite the sentence correctly. If a sentence is correct, make no changes.

1. Ravens are very clever birds.

   _____

   _____

2. The bald eagle are the symbol of the United States and its national bird.

   _____

   _____

3. The mockingbird imitate the calls of many different kinds of birds.

   _____

   _____

4. Cardinals likes evergreen trees for their nests.

   _____

   _____

5. A robin likes earthworms.

   _____

   _____

6. Urban pigeons lives in towns and cities.

   _____

   _____

CHAPTER 13   **Subject & Verb Agreement** *(pages 102–113)*

Mixed Practice: Singular and Plural Subjects

◆ Underline each subject <u>once</u> and label it *S* for singular or *P* for plural. Then underline <u>twice</u> the form of the verb in parentheses that agrees with the subject.

1. Big cats (is, are) predators.

2. The lion (is, are) the king of beasts.

3. Lions (lives, live) in the African grassland.

4. They (eats, eat) gazelles, antelopes, and zebras.

5. A male lion (weighs, weigh) almost 550 pounds.

6. Lionesses (do, does) most of the hunting for the pride.

7. All the lions (cares, care) for the lion cubs.

8. A pride (contains, contain) as many as forty lions.

9. Lions (sleeps, sleep) most of the day.

10. The lion (creeps, creep) up on its unsuspecting prey.

11. India (is, are) home to a small population of lions.

12. Cubs (has, have) a thick spotted coat.

13. They (is, are) very social animals.

14. The leopard (is, are) a relative of the lion.

15. It (hunts, hunt) smaller prey than the lion.

CHAPTER 13 Subject & Verb Agreement (pages 102–113)

Making Subject and Verb Phrases Agree

The first helping verb must agree in number with the subject.

◆ Underline each subject once and label it *S* for singular or *P* for plural. Then underline twice the helping verb in parentheses that agrees with the subject.

1. The first football game (was, were) played between Rutgers and Princeton.

2. Downhill skiers (has, have) raced at over 120 miles per hour.

3. Helmets (was, were) first introduced to the major baseball leagues in 1941.

4. Soccer (does, do) require a lot of skill.

5. Basketball (was, were) invented by James Naismith.

6. Ice hockey (is, are) played mostly in the northern states.

7. Cyclists (has, have) raced through France for many years.

8. Runners (do, does) practice for many hours.

9. The first marathon (was, were) held in Greece.

10. Tennis (was, were) played in the Middle Ages.

Name _____ Date _____

CHAPTER 13 Subject & Verb Agreement (pages 102–113)

Writing Sentences Using Subject and Verb Agreement

◆ Write five sentences that follow the instructions below.

◆ Write a sentence using *football* and a present-tense helping verb.

1. _____

_____

◆ Write a sentence using *soccer* and a past-tense helping verb.

2. _____

_____

◆ Write a sentence using *skaters* and a past-tense helping verb.

3. _____

_____

◆ Write a sentence using *skis* and a present-tense helping verb.

4. _____

_____

◆ Write a sentence using *coaches* and a past-tense helping verb.

5. _____

_____

CHAPTER 13 **Subject & Verb Agreement** *(pages 102–113)*

Correcting for Subject and Verb Agreement

◆ Rewrite each sentence in which the subject and verb do not agree. If a sentence is correct, make no changes.

1. Table tennis are becoming a popular indoor sport.

   _____

   _____

2. Jerry is playing today.

   _____

   _____

3. Floyd do like tennis.

   _____

   _____

4. Anna was introduced to cricket in England.

   _____

   _____

5. Bill were practicing hard yesterday.

   _____

   _____

CHAPTER 13 Subject & Verb Agreement (pages 102–113)

Making Subject and Verb Phrases Agree

The verb part of a contraction must agree in number with the subject.

◆ Underline each subject once. Then underline twice the contraction in parentheses that agrees with the subject.

1. Scientists (doesn't, don't) ignore the importance of ants.

2. Ants (wasn't, weren't) crawling on that plant.

3. Weaver ants (doesn't, don't) live on the ground.

4. Those ants (wasn't, weren't) unusual.

5. Some ants (doesn't, don't) live underground.

6. Some of the ants (isn't, aren't) leaving the nest.

7. I (hasn't, haven't) ever seen a herdsman ant.

8. The queen and the workers (hasn't, haven't) arrived yet.

9. That ant (isn't, aren't) crawling very fast along the garden path.

10. Aphids and mealybugs (doesn't, don't) like any kind of ants.

CHAPTER 13 **Subject & Verb Agreement** *(pages 102–113)*

Correcting for Subject and Verb Agreement

◆ Rewrite each sentence in which the subject and verb do not agree. If a sentence is correct, make no changes.

1. Herdsman ants doesn't like to stay in one place.

   _____

   _____

2. Plants aren't always homes for ants.

   _____

   _____

3. Some ants hasn't been studied yet.

   _____

   _____

4. Ants and plants doesn't always support each other.

   _____

   _____

5. Those ants weren't very large.

   _____

   _____

CHAPTER 13 Subject & Verb Agreement (pages 102–113)

Making Interrupted Subjects and Verbs Agree

The agreement of a verb with its subject is not changed by any interrupting words.

◆ Underline each subject once and label it *S* for singular or *P* for plural. Then underline twice the form of the verb in parentheses that agrees with the subject.

1. The car with the rainbow on its door (sits, sit) on the pit road.

2. The drivers at the track (seems, seem) friendly.

3. Throughout the years the friendship among the drivers (has, have) remained strong.

4. The TV announcers, along with the fans, (enjoys, enjoy) a good race.

5. The driver with the most wins this year (is, are) Dale Jarrett.

6. The driver in the shiny black car (was, were) very nervous.

7. People like Jeff Gordon (appears, appear) self-confident.

8. The three drivers from South Carolina (is, are) leading the field.

9. The paint on the new car at the track (was, were) beautiful and bright.

10. A rainbow of colors (decorates, decorate) the hood of the car.

CHAPTER 13   **Subject & Verb Agreement** *(pages 102–113)*

Correcting for Subject and Verb Agreement

◆ Rewrite the sentences in which the subject and verb do not agree. If a sentence is correct, make no changes.

1. The announcers from the TV station at the track is preparing for the race.

   _____

   _____

2. The fans, in addition to the announcers, are waiting for the green flag.

   _____

   _____

3. The drivers in the red and white cars is on the same winning team.

   _____

   _____

4. The driver with the fewest wrecks on his record is Mark Martin.

   _____

   _____

5. The track with the most dangerous turns are in New York.

   _____

   _____

CHAPTER 13   Subject & Verb Agreement (pages 102–113)

Making Subjects and Verbs in Inverted Order Agree

The subject and verb of an inverted sentence must agree in number.

◆ Underline each subject once and label it *S* for singular or *P* for plural. Then underline twice the form of the verb in parentheses that agrees with the subject.

1. There (is, are) only one baseball game after school this week.

2. When (does, do) your sister Maria pitch?

3. (Has, Have) your practices for games been challenging this year?

4. Here (is, are) my glove for the catcher.

5. In the dugout there (was, were) two heavy bags full of bats.

6. Where (was, were) the catcher at four o'clock yesterday afternoon?

7. On top of the pitcher's mound (stands, stand) a strong pitcher.

8. (Does, Do) Tito and his brother stay after practice?

9. Here (is, are) some socks from my bag.

10. (Was, Were) there any foul balls in the game last night?

CHAPTER 13　Subject & Verb Agreement *(pages 102–113)*

Writing Sentences Using Subject and Verb Agreement

◆ Write four sentences, following the instructions below.

◆ Write a sentence that begins with the word *here.*

1. _____

_____

◆ Write a question.

2. _____

_____

◆ Write a sentence that begins with the word *there.*

3. _____

_____

◆ Write a sentence that begins with a prepositional phrase and is in inverted order.

4. _____

_____

CHAPTER 13 **Subject & Verb Agreement** *(pages 102–113)*

Correcting for Subject and Verb Agreement

◆ Rewrite correctly each sentence in which the subject and verb do not agree. If a sentence is correct, make no changes.

1. When does the players arrive?

_____

_____

2. On the bus were two of my favorite gloves.

_____

_____

3. Here are the umpire.

_____

_____

4. There was two mascots for our team last year.

_____

_____

5. By the pitcher's mound was a small glove.

_____

_____

6. Do that glove belong to one of the infielders?

_____

_____

CHAPTER 13 **Subject & Verb Agreement** *(pages 102–113)*

Mixed Practice: Subject and Verb Agreement

◆ Underline each subject once. Then underline twice the form of the verb in parentheses that agrees with the subject.

1. The largest cat in the Americas (is, are) the jaguar.

2. Elephants in Africa (has, have) large ears and flat heads.

3. In the jungle (roam, roams) many wild animals.

4. A queen ant in a colony (lives, live) about ten to twenty years.

5. There (was, were) two alligators in the mud at the edge of the lake.

6. A jellyfish (has, have) little or no color.

7. Bees (doesn't, don't) want to be disturbed.

8. When (do, does) the birds migrate?

9. (Wasn't, Weren't) those birds unusual?

10. The ostrich (is, are) known for its speed.

11. Cheetahs (has, have) run at over sixty miles per hour.

12. There (isn't, aren't) many gray wolves left.

13. The dry deserts of Saudi Arabia (contains, contain) many types of beetles.

14. In the mountains (is, are) many types of sheep.

15. Sharks (do, does) swim constantly.

CHAPTER 13   **Subject & Verb Agreement** *(pages 102–113)*

Making Verbs Agree with Compound Subjects

When subjects are joined by *and*, the verb is usually plural.

When subjects are joined by *or*, *either/or*, or *neither/nor*, the verb should agree with the closer subject.

◆ <u>Underline</u> the correct form of the verb in parentheses.

1. The sun and the moon (seems, seem) almost the same size in the sky.

2. Saturn and Jupiter (has, have) moons.

3. Comets and meteors (travels, travel) through space.

4. Either that moon or that planet (is, are) rising in the east.

5. Neither Mercury nor Venus (is, are) cold.

6. Pluto and Neptune (has, have) no life.

7. Neither wind nor rain (occurs, occur) on the surface of the moon.

8. Either Venus or Mars (has, have) clouds.

9. Some asteroids and comets (passes, pass) close to Earth.

10. The sun and the moon (sets, set) in the west.

CHAPTER 13 **Subject & Verb Agreement** *(pages 102–113)*

Making Verbs Agree with Compound Subjects

◆ <u>Underline</u> the correct form of the verb in parentheses.

1. Sopranos and tenors (sings, sing) the high parts.

2. Either the altos or the basses (has, have) the harmony.

3. Neither the sopranos nor the altos (remembers, remember) their cues.

4. The piano and the flutes (plays, play) the introduction.

5. The drums and the oboe (starts, start) the second section.

6. The piano and the drums (is, are) considered percussion instruments.

7. Neither the trumpets nor the trombones (has, have) the melody.

8. Either the soloist or the conductor (bows, bow) after the music is over.

9. The clarinets and the oboes (sounds, sound) similar.

10. Neither the saxophones nor the piccolo (has, have) a part in this song.

CHAPTER 13 Subject & Verb Agreement *(pages 102–113)*

Making Verbs Agree with Compound Subjects

◆ <u>Underline</u> the correct form of the verb in parentheses.

1. Juan and his brothers (was, were) musicians.

2. The basses or the tenors (has, have) the practice rooms now.

3. The chimes and the triangle often (ring, rings) together.

4. That old, broken piano and those new flutes (was, were) given away.

5. Sopranos and altos (is, are) going to practice tomorrow.

6. The guitarist and the brass players (is, are) working up a new number.

7. The director and the jazz band (has, have) been practicing.

8. My sister and I (plans, plan) to attend the concert.

CHAPTER 13 **Subject & Verb Agreement** *(pages 102–113)*

Correcting for Subject and Verb Agreement

◆ Rewrite the sentences in which the subject and verb do not agree. If a sentence is correct, make no changes.

1. My flute and the twins' clarinets is out of tune again.

   _____

   _____

2. The woodwinds and the brass horns have the best parts in the concert.

   _____

   _____

3. The soloist and the altos likes to sing harmony together.

   _____

   _____

4. Neither Katharine's reed nor Michael's keys was broken in practice.

   _____

   _____

5. Either the bassoons or the tuba were flat during the recital.

   _____

   _____

CHAPTER 13   Subject & Verb Agreement *(pages 102–113)*

Making Verbs Agree with Collective Nouns

Use a singular verb with a collective noun subject that is thought of as a unit.
Use a plural verb with a collective noun that is thought of as individuals.

◆ <u>Underline</u> the correct form of the verb in parentheses.

1. A large and curious crowd (has, have) gathered at the dock.

2. The ship's crew (is, are) arguing over the type of sails to use.

3. A flock of seagulls (flies, fly) low in the sky.

4. The band (tunes, tune) their instruments before they play for the sailors.

5. The judging committee (makes, make) a final inspection of the ship.

6. The captain's family (wishes, wish) him good luck.

7. The sailors' league (checks, check) the boat carefully.

8. The team (disagrees, disagree) over the official start time for the race.

9. This class of boats (is, are) very fast.

10. A pod of dolphins (swims, swim) with the boat during the first part of the race.

CHAPTER 13 **Subject & Verb Agreement** (pages 102–113)

....

Correcting for Subject and Verb Agreement

◆ Rewrite each sentence in which the subject and verb do not agree. If a sentence is correct, make no changes.

1. The orchestra plays every night on the cruise ship.

   _____

   _____

2. A flock of gulls land on the deck of the big ship every afternoon.

   _____

   _____

3. My family like sailing.

   _____

   _____

4. The enthusiastic crowd cheers loudly for its favorite boat.

   _____

   _____

5. The crew prepare for a long race.

   _____

   _____

Name _____ Date _____

Mixed Practice: Subject and Verb Agreement

◆ <u>Underline</u> the form of the verb in parentheses that agrees with the subject.

1. An ant colony (is, are) very complex.

2. Termites and ants (does, do) a lot of damage to homes and lawns.

3. In Texas, bees and ants (is, are) considered pests by many people.

4. A swarm (flies, fly) to find its new home.

5. People and animals (has, have) been disturbed by ants.

6. Either ants or bees (stings, sting) people.

7. The cattle herd (avoids, avoid) ant mounds.

8. Neither fleas nor ticks (are, is) very pleasant to encounter.

9. Either termites or ants (damages, damage) homes.

10. A termite colony (does, do) need to be watched carefully.

11. Fire ants (has, have) particularly painful stings.

12. Burning sensations like fire (is, are) the painful reminder of the sting of these ants.

13. There (has, have) always been many kinds of termites in wooded areas.

14. (Doesn't, Don't) hungry termites silently eat away at all the wood in homes?

15. Warm areas of the country (has, have) more problems with ants and termites than cooler areas.

CHAPTER 13 Subject & Verb Agreement *(pages 102–113)*

Making Verbs Agree with *You* and *I*

◆ <u>Underline</u> the correct form of the verb in parentheses.

1. I (likes, like) history class.

2. You (is, are) the best student in our mathematics class.

3. I (has, have) some homework.

4. You (has, have) a report to prepare for geography class tomorrow.

5. We (was, were) in English class.

6. You (needs, need) Internet access to finish your report.

7. You (was, were) very amusing in this year's school play.

8. This year you should (studies, study) hard.

9. I always (wears, wear) this old shirt to gym class.

10. You (has, have) a lot of homework to do this weekend.

Name _____ Date _____

CHAPTER 13 Subject & Verb Agreement *(pages 102–113)*

Correcting for Subject and Verb Agreement

◆ Rewrite each sentence in which the subject and verb do not agree. If a sentence is correct, make no changes.

1. I likes my math class this year.

   _____

   _____

2. You reads many nonfiction books.

   _____

   _____

3. I enjoy science.

   _____

   _____

4. You finish your math homework quickly.

   _____

   _____

5. I types faster than you.

   _____

   _____

CHAPTER 13 **Subject & Verb Agreement** *(pages 102–113)*

Making Verbs Agree with Indefinite Pronouns

A verb must agree in number with an indefinite pronoun used as a subject.

◆ Underline each subject once and label it *S* for singular or *P* for plural. Then underline twice the form of the verb in parentheses that agrees with the subject.

1. Many of the stadium lights (has, have) burned out.

2. Each of our soccer players (is, are) wearing green shorts.

3. A few of the uniforms (was, were) the wrong size.

4. One of those players (is, are) hurt.

5. Somebody on the team (plays, play) very aggressively.

6. Either of the two game plans (is, are) workable.

7. Several on the team (has, have) worked very hard.

8. Everybody on the team (does, do) practice almost every day.

9. Many on the team (has, have) their own soccer balls.

10. No one at the game (was, were) from middle school.

CHAPTER 13 Subject & Verb Agreement (pages 102–113)

Making Verbs Agree with Indefinite Pronouns

◆ Underline each subject once and label it S for singular or P for plural. Then underline twice the form of the verb in parentheses that agrees with the subject.

1. One of the suitcases (has, have) a hole in it.

2. Each of the tourists (has, have) eaten some dinner in the small café.

3. Several of my friends (takes, take) pictures.

4. (Has, Have) everyone slept well?

5. Neither of the twins (has, have) ever gone to the beach.

6. Both of the tickets (has, have) been ordered.

7. Nobody (was, were) waiting at the train station.

8. Many of the students on our bus (listens, listen) to their headphones.

9. Everybody on the plane (cheers, cheer) loudly when we arrive.

10. Somebody in our hotel (is, are) a singer.

Name _____ Date _____

Writing Sentences with Indefinite Pronouns

◆ Write five sentences, using the following indefinite pronouns as subjects.

◆ many

1. _____

_____

◆ few

2. _____

_____

◆ both

3. _____

_____

◆ nobody

4. _____

_____

◆ someone

5. _____

_____

CHAPTER 13 Subject & Verb Agreement *(pages 102–113)*

Correcting for Subject and Verb Agreement

◆ Rewrite each sentence in which the subject and verb do not agree. If a sentence is correct, make no changes.

1. A few of the suitcases is missing.

   _____

   _____

2. Several of the tourists are tired.

   _____

   _____

3. No one like our hotel.

   _____

   _____

4. Many of the sightseers does enjoy travel.

   _____

   _____

5. Few want to return home.

   _____

   _____

CHAPTER 13 Subject & Verb Agreement *(pages 102–113)*

Mixed Practice: Subject and Verb Agreement

◆ <u>Underline</u> the correct form of the verb in parentheses.

1. Coins (has, have) been around for more than 2,500 years.

2. Once only kings and rich people (was, were) coin collectors.

3. Now more than five million people throughout the world (takes, take) part in this hobby.

4. Many of the collectors (does, do) it as an investment.

5. This hobby (is, are) often begun with just a handful of pennies.

6. There (is, are) a few pennies with a value of $115!

7. A Jefferson nickel or a Roosevelt dime (is, are) also a good addition to a collection.

8. The condition of rare coins (is, are) very important to buyers.

9. Collectors (doesn't, don't) hold any of the coins in their hands.

10. The moisture from hands (has, have) stained many valuable coins.

11. Coin dealers across the country (rates, rate) coins.

12. One of the best ratings (is, are) "extremely fine."

13. The surfaces of these coins (shows, show) little or no wear.

14. Pennies in "extremely fine" condition (is, are) worth twenty-five cents.

15. (Has, Have) you ever wanted to start a coin collection?

CHAPTER 14 Using Adjectives and Adverbs *(pages 114–119)*

Identifying the Degree of Comparison

◆ Label each underlined adjective or adverb *P* for positive, *C* for comparative, or *S* for superlative.

1. Of the mammals on both land and sea, the blue whale is the <u>largest</u>.

2. Scientists have recently discovered the <u>smallest</u> mammal.

3. The <u>tiny</u> rodent is less than an inch long.

4. A cheetah can run <u>faster</u> than a lion.

5. A baby orca <u>rapidly</u> puts on weight.

6. A pack of wolves will hunt <u>larger</u> prey than a single wolf will hunt.

7. A peacock has the <u>most impressive</u> display of feathers.

8. Does the snail crawl <u>more slowly</u> than the turtle?

9. Of all the fish in the river, that salmon jumps <u>highest</u>.

10. A cobra's venom is <u>poisonous</u>.

CHAPTER 14 **Using Adjectives and Adverbs** *(pages 114–119)*

Forming Regular Comparisons of Modifiers

◆ Read the following sentences aloud, trying out each word or group of words in parentheses. Then read the sentence aloud again, <u>underlining</u> the correct word or group of words.

1. Paul is the (tallest, most tall) member of the basketball team.

2. Bob runs (quicklier, more quickly) than Larry does.

3. Coach is one of the (helpfulest, most helpful) people I know.

4. The crowd stared (curiouslier, more curiously) at the other team than they did at us.

5. Gene plays his position (powerfullest, most powerfully) of all the team members.

6. That was the (longest, most long) game this year.

7. Danny made the (beautifullest, most beautiful) shot of the whole game.

8. The game was over (sooner, more soon) than I expected.

9. Our coach was (happier, more happy) than the other coach.

10. We won by the (narrowest, most narrow) margin all season.

CHAPTER 14 **Using Adjectives and Adverbs** (pages 114–119)

Forming the Comparison of Modifiers

◆ Write each modifier's comparative and superlative forms.

1. quick _____

2. merrily _____

3. cold _____

4. curious _____

5. quiet _____

6. dangerous _____

7. neatly _____

8. early _____

9. slowly _____

10. rapidly _____

11. careful _____

12. weakly _____

13. great _____

14. dry _____

15. big _____

Name _____ Date _____

Using the Correct Form of Modifiers

◆ <u>Underline</u> the correct modifier in each sentence.

1. Marty wasn't sure which was (easier, easiest), rowing or paddling.

2. Does the canoe or the rowboat glide (faster, fastest)?

3. Juan faced the situation (more bravely, most bravely) than I did.

4. Of the two boats, which do you think is (bigger, biggest)?

5. Of the five rowers, Barry rows the (more skillfully, most skillfully).

6. Which of the two rowing teams is (more powerful, most powerful)?

7. Of the ten races I've seen this year, this was (more enjoyable, most enjoyable).

8. Joe is the (stronger, strongest) member of the rowing team.

9. A canoe can move (more quickly, most quickly) than a barge.

10. Which race was the (shorter, shortest), the first or the last?

CHAPTER 14 Using Adjectives and Adverbs *(pages 114–119)*

Forming Comparisons of Modifiers

◆ Read the following sentences aloud, trying out each word in parentheses. Then read each sentence aloud again, underlining the correct word.

1. This is the (goodest, best) place for a picnic.

2. Did you do (weller, better) in the potato sack races than Sita?

3. Sue ate the (less, least) amount of food of anyone at the picnic.

4. Margaret had (mucher, more) chicken than Sharlene had.

5. That was the (baddest, worst) potato salad I have ever eaten.

6. The games were the (best, better) we have ever had.

7. The planning of the picnic went (well, good).

8. The food preparation was (difficulter, more difficult) than last year.

9. There were (more, most) vegetarians this year.

10. There was (less, lesser) food left over.

Name _____ Date _____

Supplying the Correct Form of Modifiers

◆ Read the first sentence in each group. Then write the comparative and superlative forms of the underlined modifier in the blanks of the two sentences below it.

1. I have <u>little</u> interest in science fiction.

   I have _____ interest in fables.

   I have the _____ interest in biographies.

2. You read quite <u>well</u>.

   You read _____ than my sister.

   You read the _____ of all the students in my class.

3. The book this week is <u>good</u>.

   I think it is _____ than last week's book.

   In fact, it is the _____ book I have read so far this month.

4. <u>Many</u> people in my class buy books.

   _____ people use the library.

   However, _____ people prefer to borrow books from one another.

5. I feel <u>bad</u> about the ending of this book.

   I felt _____ about the ending of last week's book.

   Two weeks ago, I felt _____ of all.

Name _____ Date _____

Using the Correct Form of Modifiers

◆ If a modifier is used incorrectly, rewrite the sentence. If the sentence is correct, make no changes.

1. Which do you like goodest, animal stories or science fiction?

   _____

   _____

2. That book is definitely the worst one I have read all year.

   _____

   _____

3. Leslie couldn't decide which book she liked most, the mystery or the fairy tale.

   _____

   _____

4. Who reads fastest, Lee or Shirley?

   _____

   _____

5. That science encyclopedia is the bigger book in the whole library.

   _____

   _____

CHAPTER 14 **Using Adjectives and Adverbs** *(pages 114–119)*

Mixed Practice: Modifiers

◆ Find and <u>underline</u> each incorrect modifier. Then write it correctly above.

1. Which type of music do you like best, classical or jazz?

2. Of the three composers, Mozart is the more challenging.

3. Is jazz, classical, or pop the harder to play on the guitar?

4. Who wrote the best music, Ludwig van Beethoven or Johann Sebastian Bach?

5. That composition was the more difficult piece I have ever played.

6. That song was without a doubt the worse song I've heard all year!

7. Which instrument plays most loudly, the tuba or the piccolo?

8. Of all the instruments my brother can play, I like the baritone the less.

9. Of all my music, I have played the Mozart piece more recently.

10. Which composition came earliest in the program, "Für Elise" or the *Moonlight Sonata*?

11. I am least eager to hear the symphony than Cynthia is.

12. He couldn't decide which he liked most, the trumpet or the flute.

CHAPTER 14 Using Adjectives and Adverbs (pages 114–119)

Identifying Problems with *Other* or *Else*

◆ Read the following sentences, looking for problems with *other* or *else*. Write *C* in the blank if the sentence is correct and *I* if the sentence is incorrect.

_____ 1. Harry learned his lines more quickly than anyone in the play.

_____ 2. Our play was better than any other play performed by seventh graders.

_____ 3. Sally sings better than any singer in the play.

_____ 4. Mrs. Constanza dedicated more of her time to the production than anyone else at our school.

_____ 5. My mom took more pictures of the dress rehearsal than anyone did.

_____ 6. Sharon had stage fright worse than anyone in the cast.

_____ 7. No one was as calm as Juan.

_____ 8. Jori got the part because she is taller than any other student who auditioned.

_____ 9. Mrs. Constanza was more nervous than the other teachers.

_____ 10. Sam sang louder than any other performer in the cast.

_____ 11. Barry recited more lines of dialogue than any other cast member.

_____ 12. Chen practiced his lines for this play harder than anyone.

CHAPTER 14   **Using Adjectives and Adverbs**   *(pages 114–119)*

Correcting Errors with *Other* or *Else*

◆ Rewrite the incorrect sentences from the preceding exercise, using *other* or *else* correctly.

1. _____

   _____

2. _____

   _____

3. _____

   _____

4. _____

   _____

5. _____

   _____

6. _____

   _____

CHAPTER 14   Using Adjectives and Adverbs   *(pages 114–119)*

Identifying Double Comparisons

◆ Read the following sentences, looking for problems with double comparisons. Write *C* in the blank if the sentence is correct and *I* if the sentence is incorrect.

_____ 1. The weather in Texas is more drier than the weather in Pennsylvania.

_____ 2. Some people think the hills of Austin are prettier than the hills of Pittsburgh.

_____ 3. The terrain west of Austin becomes more steeper than the terrain east of Austin.

_____ 4. Spanish explorers arrived in Texas earlier than the French arrived in Pennsylvania.

_____ 5. People in Texas can swim outside for a more longer time than people in Pennsylvania.

_____ 6. Many agree that sunrises on the Gulf Coast are the prettiest they have ever seen.

_____ 7. Most Texans believe that their chili is more tastier than Northern chili.

_____ 8. Texas is the most biggest state in the continental United States.

_____ 9. Some of the most interesting architecture in the state can be seen in Austin.

_____ 10. Winter in Texas is warmer than in Pennsylvania.

CHAPTER 14   Using Adjectives and Adverbs   *(pages 114–119)*

Correcting Errors with Double Comparisons

◆ Rewrite the incorrect sentences from the preceding exercise so that there are no double comparisons.

1. _____

   _____

2. _____

   _____

3. _____

   _____

4. _____

   _____

5. _____

   _____

CHAPTER 14 **Using Adjectives and Adverbs** *(pages 114–119)*

Identifying Double Negatives

◆ Read each of the following sentences, looking for double negatives. Write *C* in the blank if the sentence is correct and *I* if the sentence is incorrect.

_____ 1. Porpoises don't have no gills.

_____ 2. Some salamanders don't have no lungs, so they breathe through their skin.

_____ 3. Most people didn't know anything about dodo birds until they became extinct.

_____ 4. Some squirrels can't never find the acorns they bury.

_____ 5. An eagle won't let anything harm its chicks.

_____ 6. That mongoose has not done nothing about the cobra in the garden.

_____ 7. The scientists have never seen that species before.

_____ 8. There is no way to protect endangered species without educating the public.

_____ 9. That caterpillar hasn't never stopped eating parsley.

_____ 10. A newly hatched hornbill cannot leave the nest until its feathers grow.

CHAPTER 14 **Using Adjectives and Adverbs** *(pages 114–119)*

Correcting Errors with Double Negatives

◆ Rewrite the incorrect sentences from the preceding exercise, eliminating the double negatives.

1. _____

_____

2. _____

_____

3. _____

_____

4. _____

_____

5. _____

_____

CHAPTER 14 Using Adjectives and Adverbs *(pages 114–119)*

Using *Good* or *Well*

◆ Write *good* or *well* to correctly complete each sentence.

1. Vacuum the rug _____.

2. Janice dances _____.

3. I feel quite _____.

4. The steak looks _____.

5. It's running _____.

6. The lunch tasted _____.

7. The Lions played _____.

8. That rain feels _____.

9. Sandra dives _____.

10. Tim's voice is _____.

Name _____ Date _____

Correcting Errors with *Good* or *Well*

◆ Rewrite the following sentences if they contain errors with *good* or *well*. If a sentence is correct, make no changes.

1. The new band sounds good.

    _____

    _____

2. They played good at their first concert.

    _____

    _____

3. The conductor was not feeling well.

    _____

    _____

4. The flute section did well with the solo.

    _____

    _____

CHAPTER 14 Using Adjectives and Adverbs (pages 114–119)

Mixed Practice: Modifiers

◆ Correct any misused modifiers in the following paragraphs.

1.   Which is most famous, a rabbit or a hare? There's no question about it. Rabbits win every time. After all, who hasn't never read about Bugs Bunny, Peter Rabbit, or Brer Rabbit?

2.   A rabbit is different from a hare. Of the two animals, the rabbit is smallest. A rabbit has more shorter ears and legs than a hare has. Rabbits build their nests in burrows. Their young are born blind. A newly born hare, on the other hand, has fully opened eyes. In addition, a rabbit doesn't have no hair when it is born, but a newborn hare has a full coat of hair. Newborn hares are able to hop more earlier than baby rabbits can. Young hares are born in an open field. As a result they can take better care of themselves sooner than young rabbits can.

3.   All rabbits and hares run and jump good. They jump faster than any animal in the forest. A running jackrabbit takes a more higher leap every sixth stride. By doing this, it is able to look around for any possible danger. The strong hind legs of rabbits make them fast runners.

4.   Both kinds of animals are more activer at night than in the day. Rabbits and hares eat plants, but they don't eat no meat.

A Writer's Glossary of Usage   *(pages 120–129)*

Finding the Correct Word

◆ <u>Underline</u> the word in parentheses that correctly completes each sentence.

1. (Among, Between) the many skills to master, none is more important than reading.

2. You have (all ready, already) learned some reading strategies.

3. The ability to read well (affects, effects) your life.

4. It has a direct (affect, effect) on whether you enjoy reading.

5. It also can (affect, effect) your comprehension.

6. Reading fiction, for example, (ain't, isn't) always easy because a plot has many twists and turns.

7. A varied (amount, number) of strategies are available to help you.

8. When you begin reading, you need to create (a, an) interaction (among, between) yourself and the text.

9. (A, An) reading log allows you to record (many, a lot) of your thoughts.

10. With an open mind and a reading log, you are (all ready, already) to start an exciting journey.

Name _____ Date _____

A Writer's Glossary of Usage *(pages 120–129)*

Recognizing Correct Usage

◆ Look at the underlined words in the following paragraph. If a word is used correctly, write *C* above it. If a word is used incorrectly, write the correct form of the word.

Most teachers will <u>except</u> any reading log response to the text <u>except</u> a plot summary. Any place in the text where you find a problem <u>at</u>, you should list possible questions. If a certain character <u>effects</u> you, you can describe your feelings. <u>Anywheres</u> you find a line or passage you especially like, explain the <u>effect</u> it has on you. If a situation reminds you of a book you have <u>all ready</u> read, compare the similarities <u>between</u> the two. With these strategies, you can gain a large <u>amount</u> of practice. You should then be <u>all ready</u> for an intelligent class discussion.

A Writer's Glossary of Usage   *(pages 120–129)*

Finding the Correct Word

◆ <u>Underline</u> the word in parentheses that correctly completes each sentence.

1. (Fewer, Less) people depend solely on automobiles for transportation than ever before.

2. (Its, It's) not uncommon for people to travel by helicopter, dogsled, canoe, kayak, or ferry boat.

3. You (can, may) wish to travel on a cruise ship.

4. The ship might (bring, take) you close enough to view beautiful scenery.

5. You never could (have, of) seen as much by car.

6. Travel by water is also a (good, well) way to visit interesting cities and sights.

7. Be sure to (bring, take) a journal with you!

8. If you watch closely, a pod of whales (may, might) surface near the ship.

9. Possibly you'll spy an eagle atop (its, it's) nest.

10. When the ship sails (in, into) each port, you might ride ashore in a boat called a tender.

A Writer's Glossary of Usage   *(pages 120–129)*

Recognizing Correct Usage

◆ Look at the underlined words in the following paragraph. If a word is used correctly, write *C* above it. If a word is used incorrectly, write the correct form of the word.

Kayaks <u>can</u> be navigated through the canals in the city of Ketchikan. <u>Its</u> also known as "the Salmon Capital of the World." You might feel <u>badly</u> about missing a feast if you don't go to a salmon bake. One spectacular sight is the rain forest with <u>its</u> collection of totem poles. In Juneau, you <u>can</u> find it difficult to walk on the steep streets. If you <u>badly</u> want to walk on ice, take a helicopter ride to Mendenhall Glacier. After most cruise ships leave Juneau, they travel <u>into</u> Glacier Bay. The glaciers, which gleam like diamonds, <u>don't</u> <u>hardly</u> seem real. Although Sitka has <u>less</u> people than Ketchikan and Juneau, it is a historic place. You <u>doesn't</u> want to miss seeing the icons <u>in</u> St. Michael's Cathedral.

A Writer's Glossary of Usage   *(pages 120–129)*

Finding the Correct Word

◆ <u>Underline</u> the word in parentheses that correctly completes each sentence.

1. Expectations receive more attention now (than, then) in the (passed, past).

2. When teachers (raise, rise) their expectations, students usually respond.

3. This concept results in (learning, teaching) students to (set, sit) higher goals.

4. When students (raise, rise) to a new level, (than, then) they are often rewarded.

5. As a result, students (learn, teach) the connection that (lays, lies) between success and recognition.

6. The recognition (that, which, who) students receive comes in a variety of forms.

7. Some teachers (shall, will) display superior work on the bulletin board.

8. This reward (leaves, lets) students enjoy peer recognition also.

9. Students (that, who) have reached or (passed, past) certain goals sometimes receive certificates.

10. Complimentary postcards, (which, who) praise a student's efforts, may be sent to parents.

A Writer's Glossary of Usage (pages 120–129)

Using Correct Forms of Verbs

◆ Look at the underlined verbs. If the verb is used correctly, write *C* above it. If the verb is used incorrectly, write the correct form of the verb.

The teacher informs the students that failure often <u>lays</u> in a lack of effort.

The students <u>set</u> attentively through the class. They are <u>sitting</u> their goals for

success. The teacher further explains that they should be <u>setting</u> their minds on

their goals. A goal helps <u>sit</u> the tone for achievement. As a result, the teacher

who <u>raises</u> the issue often sees a sharp <u>raise</u> in students' attitudes. At the end

of the year, many students will have <u>raised</u> their grades. Their self-esteem will

have <u>raised</u> also.

A Writer's Glossary of Usage   *(pages 120–129)*

Finding the Correct Word

◆ <u>Underline</u> the word in parentheses that correctly completes each sentence.

1. (Their, There, They're) will likely be a variety of assignments for special credit in (your, you're) geography class.

2. Map drawing allows students (to, too, two) visualize the shape of (that, that there) particular country.

3. Filling in names of important cities helps with learning (to, too, two).

4. (Them, Those) maps are both informative and creative.

5. Frequently guest speakers who (use to, used to) live in another country give interesting and valuable talks.

6. (Those, Them) interested in a particular country might do more research.

7. Students (who, whom) enjoy cooperative learning might prefer to work in groups of (to, too, two) or more.

8. Students have great fun when they plan a trip to the country of (their, there, they're) choice.

9. (Their, There, They're) required to calculate the mileage of the trip (their, there, they're).

10. When (your, you're) deciding what clothes to pack for (this, this here) trip, think about the climate of the country you are visiting.

A Writer's Glossary of Usage *(pages 120–129)*

Recognizing Correct Usage

◆ Look at the underlined words. If a word is used correctly, write *C* above it. If a word is used incorrectly, write the correct form of the word.

Learning about other people's culture is exciting because <u>theirs</u> is different from your own. A cultural-awareness day serves <u>too</u> purposes. <u>Them</u> are the enjoyment and involvement of everyone in class. Advanced planning is necessary to decide <u>whose</u> responsible for different projects. One group, <u>whose</u> focus is language, might learn key phrases to teach <u>too</u> the class. Another might concentrate on the food of <u>that there</u> country. Students <u>who</u> like to cook could prepare native dishes. Others <u>whom</u> are artistic might design costumes worn in <u>that</u> country. <u>Them</u> games that are popular <u>they're</u> could be played too. At the end of the project, <u>your</u> certain to have come a long <u>ways</u> in understanding another culture.

A Writer's Glossary of Usage   *(pages 120–129)*

Mixed Practice: Usage

◆ <u>Underline</u> the word in parentheses that correctly completes each sentence.

1. (Shall, Will) we take a glimpse (in, into) the center of Europe?

2. One fascinating country (whose, who's) neutrality is known (everywhere, everywheres) is Switzerland.

3. Switzerland is (good, well) known for its mountains.

4. The Swiss Alps, (that, which, who) are one of three geographical regions in the country, are also (among, between) the world's most famous mountain ranges.

5. (Their, There, They're) also part of the literary (passed, past) in Johanna Spyri's story of Heidi.

6. If you travel to Mount Titlis, you (can, may) eat in a mountaintop restaurant.

7. (Theirs, There's) (not any, not no) better dining experience (than, then) fondue.

8. (Fewer, Less) sights are more interesting than watching the cows descend from the mountains.

9. The cows have large cowbells around (their, there, they're) necks and are often decorated with ribbons and flowers.

10. In no place (accept, except) Bern, the capital of Switzerland, (shall, will) you find a bear pit in the middle of the city!

A Writer's Glossary of Usage   *(pages 120–129)*

Mixed Practice: Usage

◆ <u>Underline</u> the word in parentheses that correctly completes each sentence.

1. My sister (threw, through) the book on the couch with a sigh.

2. "I (knew, new) how the mystery would end before I even finished it," she said.

3. "I wish I could find a (good, well) writer."

4. "(Can, May) I give you some (advice, advise)?" I asked.

5. "Sure, (you're, your) suggestion probably can't make it any worse."

6. I (set, sat) my favorite science fiction book on the table between us.

7. "You (know, no) I don't like science fiction," she complained.

8. "Try it," I said. "If you don't like it, you don't have to read the (whole, hole) thing."

9. "Okay," she said with a sigh. "I (accept, except) your offer."

10. "Don't complain to me if the vocabulary is (to, too) hard for you," I added with a laugh. I had to duck the pillow she tossed at me.

CHAPTER 15　Capitalization　(pages 130–141)

Capitalizing First Words and *I*

◆ <u>Underline</u> and write correctly each word that should be capitalized.

1. before snowy Canada converted to the metric system, my family took a trip to Montreal.

2. montreal is a beautiful city.

3. it has incredible museums.

4. consumer goods in Montreal were measured by the Canadian system.

5. for example, gasoline was sold by the imperial gallon.

6. an imperial gallon is equal to approximately five U.S. quarts.

7. the imperial gallon sold for about $1.50, but the U.S. gallon cost about $1.15.

8. my father asked me to calculate the relative cost of gasoline in Canada and the United States.

9. furthermore, i had to figure which price was the better bargain.

10. i'll never forget how long it took me to calculate the costs.

11. the vacation was delayed until i could figure out the relative costs.

12. thank goodness Canada has converted to the metric system.

13. to this day i get nervous thinking about imperial gallons in wintry Canada.

14. our vacation went splendidly.

CHAPTER 15 **Capitalization**   *(pages 130–141)*

Using Capital Letters

◆ Rewrite the following letter, adding capital letters where needed.

dear Mr. Grieb,

now that English class is over, i wish to thank you for talking to our class about poetry. your information was appreciated by the whole class. i found this quotation that i think you'll enjoy. Algernon Charles Swinburne wrote:

sleep; and if life were bitter to thee, pardon,

if sweet, give thanks; thou hast no more to live;

and to give thanks is good, and to forgive.

i hope that you are able to visit our English class again soon.

sincerely,

Monica

_____

_____

_____

_____

_____

_____

CHAPTER 15 Capitalization *(pages 130–141)*

Capitalizing Proper Nouns

◆ <u>Underline</u> and write correctly each word that should be capitalized.

1. Rita likes American colonial history more than her friend fred does.

2. Planter james madison called for a Constitutional Convention.

3. Back in 1786, madison wanted to revise the Articles of Confederation.

4. At first george washington was not enthusiastic.

5. Finally washington agreed with james madison and alexander hamilton that changes were needed.

6. Fifty-five delegates went to ben franklin's hometown.

7. They were to work with madison, hamilton, and franklin on the United States constitution.

8. The delegates chose washington as presiding officer.

9. james madison's plan called for a two-house Congress.

10. On the other hand, william patterson favored a one-house plan.

11. The British leader william e. gladstone greatly admired the united states constitution.

12. Twenty-six-year-old jonathan dayton was the youngest signer.

13. Eighty-one-year-old benjamin franklin was the oldest.

14. Another signer was gunning bedford, jr.

Name _____ Date _____

CHAPTER 15 **Capitalization** *(pages 130–141)*

Capitalizing Geographical Names

◆ <u>Underline</u> each word that should be capitalized.

1. In 1840, the united states had 3,000 miles of railroad track.

2. By 1850, workers were constructing railroads in all of the states east of the mississippi river.

3. One of these railroads linked new york city and buffalo, new york.

4. Others linked such cities as baltimore, maryland, and wheeling, west virginia.

5. Railway builders linked these eastern lines with lines in ohio, indiana, and illinois.

6. Railway lines went around both lake erie and lake michigan.

7. Before the railroads many depended on the mississippi river to transport goods.

8. The goods were put on ships in new orleans, louisiana.

9. The ships sailed around florida to cities in the east.

10. From the east to past the rocky mountains, north america was opened up by the railroad.

CHAPTER 15 **Capitalization** *(pages 130–141)*

Using Capital Letters

◆ <u>Underline</u> each word that should be capitalized.

1. A major peacekeeping organization was created after world war II.

2. The united nations (un) was established to ensure peace.

3. It was an effort to improve on the league of nations.

4. The league of nations was formed after wwI.

5. Almost 200 member nations support the un financially.

6. The united states senate and the house of representatives must pass the budget each year.

7. The united nations supports the world health organization and unicef.

8. The security council guides all activities of the un.

9. The general assembly includes all members of the organization.

10. The offices of the un are located in new york city.

CHAPTER 15 **Capitalization** *(pages 130–141)*

Using Capital Letters

◆ Rewrite the following sentences, adding capital letters where needed.

1. On June 28, 1919, the allies and Germany signed a treaty to end world war I.

   _____

   _____

2. The agreement was called the treaty of versailles.

   _____

   _____

3. With the support of congress, the treaty would divide the German empire into nine nations.

   _____

   _____

4. President Wilson managed to get the league of nations included as part of the treaty.

   _____

   _____

5. This accomplishment was one of Wilson's famous fourteen points.

   _____

   _____

6. The American president hoped that the league would help lessen the impact of the treaty of versailles on Germany.

   _____

   _____

CHAPTER 15 **Capitalization** *(pages 130–141)*

Using Capital Letters

◆ In preparation for proposing a peer-group organization to improve communication at your school, jot down answers to the following questions. Use capital letters where needed.

1. What will be the formal name of the organization?

   _____

   _____

2. Which school official will sponsor the organization?

   _____

   _____

3. What officers will the organization have?

   _____

   _____

4. Where will the organization meet?

   _____

   _____

5. What state or national organization will this peer group be like?

   _____

   _____

6. How will this organization improve communication?

   _____

   _____

Name _____ Date _____

CHAPTER 15 **Capitalization** *(pages 130–141)*

Using Capital Letters

◆ <u>Underline</u> each word that should be capitalized. If the sentence is correct, make no changes.

1. The fall of the school year is full of both religious and secular holidays.

2. Just as september begins, there is labor day.

3. Also in september, jews celebrate rosh hashanah.

4. The second monday of october is columbus day.

5. United nations Day is october 24.

6. By late october halloween is upon us.

7. On November 11 we celebrate veterans day.

8. On a thursday in november is thanksgiving.

9. December brings the christian season of christmas.

10. In some years during the same period, muslims begin observing ramadan.

CHAPTER 15 **Capitalization** *(pages 130–141)*

Using Capital Letters

◆ Rewrite the following paragraph, adding capital letters.

After christmas, new year's day, and martin luther king, jr., day, what is there to look forward to in february? What the winter needs is another holiday! It should be a holiday that appeals to many groups—Chinese, West Indian, Latino, and Pakistani—to name a few. Perhaps we should celebrate it on a tuesday or a thursday. It should not conflict with the days of worship for christianity, judaism, islam, and other faiths. Could it be a mixture of a fiesta and the fourth of july? The activities would start at four p.m. There would be tasty food, fun, and games. Let's have it on february 4. We'll call it february's festival day!

_____

_____

_____

_____

_____

_____

_____

_____

CHAPTER 15 **Capitalization** (pages 130–141)

Using Capital Letters

◆ In preparation for proposing a new holiday, answer the following questions. Use capital letters where needed.

1. In what month would you have the new holiday?

   _____

   _____

2. On what day of the week would you have it?

   _____

   _____

3. At what time will the holiday begin and end?

   _____

   _____

4. Why did you pick that month, day, and time?

   _____

   _____

5. What is the reason for the holiday?

   _____

   _____

6. How will you celebrate the holiday?

   _____

   _____

Name _____ Date _____

Using Capital Letters

◆ <u>Underline</u> each word that should be capitalized.

1. Can you imagine what the public thought in the old days about traveling to mars or other planets?

2. Was the spaceship the size and the shape of the washington monument?

3. Did the crew fill up the tank with pell gasoline?

4. Who besides nasa could try space travel?

5. How does a person get a road map to saturn?

6. You can't exactly go north and turn right at the planet mercury.

7. Did the astronauts travel in the *voyager* spacecraft?

8. Would the astronauts have to be able to speak russian, spanish, and computer languages?

9. They would need to have passed more science courses than physics IV and chemistry IV.

10. Do you think that the astronauts should be given the congressional medal of honor?

CHAPTER 15 **Capitalization** *(pages 130–141)*

Using Capital Letters

◆ Rewrite the following paragraph, adding capital letters where needed.

Plu is from pluto. His eyes are the size of the pancakes from the tasty maple brand of pancakes. His skin is as smooth as the ice at the metro skating rink. Toothless, he stands as tall and as bony as the eiffel tower in Paris. Plu from pluto has no arms or legs. Rapid german-like sounds come out of his toothless mouth. Through an instant translation machine borrowed from nasa, Plu asked me if I owned a fire-engine red automobile. When I told him I was too young to drive a car, he said he would settle for a ride in the *discovery* space shuttle. From what I could tell, I would have to take german I, II, and III to understand his language and physics IV to figure out how he got to earth. Unfortunately, Plu broke my computer when he tried to put his own web page on the internet.

_____

_____

_____

_____

_____

_____

_____

_____

CHAPTER 15 Capitalization *(pages 130–141)*

Using Capital Letters

◆ In preparation for writing an original story about an alien, answer the following questions. Use capital letters where needed.

1. What planet or constellation is your alien from?

   _____

   _____

2. What building, bridge, or monument in the world is about the same size as your alien?

   _____

   _____

3. What product in a grocery store most resembles the color of your alien?

   _____

   _____

4. What language on earth does its language sound like?

   _____

   _____

5. What kind of car does it prefer?

   _____

   _____

6. What kind of soft drink does it like?

   _____

   _____

CHAPTER 15 Capitalization *(pages 130–141)*

Mixed Practice: Capital Letters

◆ <u>Underline</u> each word that should be capitalized. Then answer each question if you can!

1. who was the first person to sign the declaration of independence?

   _____

2. who used a middle initial that did not stand for a middle name—harry s. truman or franklin d. roosevelt?

   _____

3. who built their empire first, the mayas or the aztecs?

   _____

4. who was raised in the midwest, jefferson or lincoln?

   _____

5. who, little orphan annie or mickey mouse, owned a dog named pluto?

   _____

6. who was the first person to walk on the moon, michael collins or neil armstrong?

   _____

7. who sold louisiana to the americans in 1803, the english or the french?

   _____

8. who was the captain of the starship *enterprise*, james kirk or alan shepherd?

   _____

CHAPTER 15 Capitalization   *(pages 130–141)*

Capitalizing Proper Adjectives

◆ <u>Underline</u> each word that should be capitalized.

1. Political candidates collect different experiences during a tour of the north american continent.

2. They travel north to the canadian border.

3. They go south as far as the mexican border.

4. They might collect swedish recipes from chefs in Minnesota.

5. They dine on chinese food in San Francisco.

6. Cheeses are given to them by the pennsylvania dutch population.

7. Samples of texas barbecue sauce are plentiful.

8. In the Empire State Building, they can feast on italian food.

9. In the South, they get bags of georgia peanuts.

10. They can sample irish stew on St. Patrick's Day.

CHAPTER 15 **Capitalization**   *(pages 130–141)*

Capitalizing Proper Adjectives

◆ Rewrite the following paragraph, adding capital letters where needed.

The european railway system is vital to the economy. An american traveler can see all of Europe from the trains. One day an american tourist can join in the scottish dances. The next day he or she can zip south to english soil and take in a Shakespearean play. However, a real shopper will use the railroad to find goods in other countries. With a longer journey, the traveler can buy the products of spanish merchants. Many seek french fashions and italian shoes. Others want german automobiles. No one wants to miss the european sights. The buildings themselves are evidence of events from roman history.

_____

_____

_____

_____

_____

_____

_____

_____

CHAPTER 15 **Capitalization** *(pages 130–141)*

Capitalizing Titles of People

◆ <u>Underline</u> each word that should be capitalized. If the sentence is correct, make no changes.

1. Have you been to mr. Brook's new chemistry laboratory?

2. Yes, mr. Brook is my sister's chemistry teacher this year.

3. He is the nephew of principal Balinger.

4. There is a huge chart hanging on the wall in the chemistry lab.

5. In the late 1800s, dr. Dimitri Mendeleev did important work.

6. Indeed, doctor, you made the study of chemistry much easier.

7. The doctor from Russia created a table for the elements.

8. dr. Mendeleev's table arranged the elements according to atomic mass.

9. In 1913, professor Henry G. J. Moseley improved on the table.

10. The professor improved on the doctor's analysis of elements.

CHAPTER 15 Capitalization *(pages 130–141)*

Using Capital Letters

◆ Rewrite the following paragraph, adding capital letters where needed.

After many medical tests on governor salem, Dr. Harry Rose found a tumor in his patient's thyroid. The doctor told the governor immediately. medical chief of staff Rose decided to treat the tumor with a radioactive isotope. Our governor asked about the treatment. As expected, dr. Rose was very informative. The doctor explained that he had used the isotope on his aunt the week before. The isotope is called iodine-131 and is very unstable. That instability helped aunt Mildred because it released radiation into her tumor. As it did for the doctor's aunt, the isotope would help shrink or destroy governor salem's tumor. The isotope of iodine, according to dr. Rose, is a doctor's friend.

_____

_____

_____

_____

_____

_____

_____

_____

CHAPTER 15　Capitalization　*(pages 130–141)*

Capitalizing Titles

◆ <u>Underline</u> each word that should be capitalized.

1. Helen is an old-fashioned teenager right out of Thorton Wilder's play *our town.*

2. Her favorite song is Katherine Lee Bates's "america the beautiful."

3. She enjoys reading articles like "essentials of good citizenship" in *reader's digest.*

4. She prefers animated films such as *the lion king* and *bambi.*

5. The fable "the tortoise and the hare" is a good example of how she leads her life.

6. She subscribes to *the new york times.*

7. It is a newspaper without comics like *for better or worse.*

8. Her idea of a romantic song is "moon river."

9. Her favorite book is *the summer of my german soldier.*

10. She wants to play Juliet in Shakespeare's *romeo and juliet.*

Name _____ Date _____

Using Capital Letters

◆ Add capital letters where needed in the following paragraphs.

1. More than 350 years ago, the inca indians of south america controlled an

    empire of almost 2,500 miles, from colombia to chile. In approximately a.d.

    1400, this tribe conquered some 10 million people living in present-day peru,

    ecuador, bolivia, western argentina, and the northern part of chile.

2. Across the many miles of the empire, the incas built a network of roads. The

    roads, however, had to run through and around the andes mountains. This feat

    would be difficult even for modern engineers.

3. Often the incas tunneled through the mountain cliffs, but they also built

    bridges. The longest of the inca bridges was made famous in the novel *the bridge*

    of san luis rey. This 148-foot suspension bridge crossed a deep ravine of the

    apurimac river. Until the bridge fell early in the 20th century, it had been in use

    longer than any other bridge in south america.

4. Because of an internal civil war in their empire, these mighty indians

    were conquered by a handful of spaniards led by francisco pizarro.

    Information about their art, culture, and village life is contained in spanish

    chronicles.

Name _____ Date _____

Mixed Practice: Capital Letters

◆ <u>Underline</u> each word that should be capitalized. Then answer each question if you can!

1. which is closer to the sun, mercury or venus?

   _____

2. what is the name of clark kent's newspaper, the daily news or the daily planet?

   _____

3. what river begins in new hampshire but is named for another state—the connecticut or the delaware?

   _____

4. what famous indian princess rescued john smith from death?

   _____

5. in what year did columbus sight land in what is now the bahamas?

   _____

6. what group first recorded the song "with a little help from my friends"?

   _____

7. what is the first monday in september called?

   _____

8. what is another name for cape canaveral in florida?

   _____

CHAPTER 16 End Marks and Commas *(pages 142–153)*

Using End Marks

Place a **period** after a statement, after an opinion, and after a command or request that, if spoken, would be made in a normal tone of voice.

Place a **question mark** after a sentence that asks a question.

Place an **exclamation point** after a sentence that states strong feeling and after a command or request that expresses great excitement.

◆ Read each sentence and then write the correct end mark.

1. Who were the first people to settle in North America

2. The Europeans found Native Americans already there in the 1400s

3. Wow, that must have been an exciting first meeting

4. Where had the Native Americans come from

5. Some thought the first Americans came from Asia

6. Others said that they came from Atlantis, an island that sank into the ocean

7. Science has another theory

8. Look at a current map of the world

9. The shapes of the continents point to a missing link between America and Asia

10. Do you think the land between the two sank into the ocean

CHAPTER 16   End Marks and Commas   *(pages 142–153)*

Using End Marks

◆ Add or change end marks where needed in the following sentences.

Have you ever heard of Beringia. According to scientists, that is the

stretch of land that once was between Asia and America Can you imagine that.

Our Earth has passed through many Ice Ages! Do you know when the last Ice

Age was About 12,000 years ago, the frozen period lowered the sea levels?

When the ice melted, land was exposed! Does that theory seem likely to you.

CHAPTER 16 End Marks and Commas   *(pages 142–153)*

Using End Marks

◆ Write the abbreviations that stand for the following items. Be sure to end them with a period when appropriate. Use a dictionary if you are not sure of an abbreviation.

1. pounds _____

2. Celsius _____

3. Road _____

4. longitude _____

5. Street _____

6. Doctor _____

7. March _____

8. Junior _____

9. meter _____

10. Friday _____

11. Tuesday _____

12. feet _____

13. December _____

CHAPTER 16   End Marks and Commas   *(pages 142–153)*

Using End Marks

◆ Add periods where needed in the following sentences.

1. It was an emergency

2. At 8:45 am, Dr Harriet L Sackel rushed from her car parked on 2422 Forest St

3. The patient was being given CPR by a Lt J W Snow

4. The lieutenant worked for the Orange County Sheriff's Department in California

5. Dr Sackel asked the officer about the man's condition

6. He gave the patient's blood pressure and pulse

7. No one knew what had happened

8. Mr Gary L Martin had been found unconscious

9. His home state on his driver's license was listed as Texas

10. Dr Sackel asked Lt Snow to call for an ambulance

Name _____ Date _____

CHAPTER 16 End Marks and Commas *(pages 142–153)*

....

Using Commas in a Series

◆ Write *C* in the blank if a sentence uses commas correctly. If a sentence uses commas incorrectly, write *I*.

_____ 1. An atom contains electrons protons and neutrons.

_____ 2. The nucleus is the center of the atom, is positively charged, and is made of protons and neutrons.

_____ 3. A neutron is located in the nucleus has no charge, and has a relative mass of 1.

_____ 4. Electrons are negatively charged, small in mass and outside the nucleus.

_____ 5. The mass of the electron is about 1/2000 of the proton and of the neutron.

◆ Write the incorrect sentences from the preceding exercise, adding commas where needed.

6. _____

_____

7. _____

_____

8. _____

_____

CHAPTER 16 **End Marks and Commas** *(pages 142–153)*

Using Commas in a Series

◆ Add commas where needed in the following sentences. If a sentence is correct as written, make no changes.

1. The home of Thomas Edison in Fort Myers was painted in 1994 1996 and 1998.

2. White is used for the exterior walls the porch and the gables.

3. The painters wash scrape and sand the surface before painting.

4. The windows and the fixtures are more difficult to paint.

5. They require small tools delicate work and careful attention.

6. Are the windows painted a robin's egg blue a navy blue or another shade of blue?

7. The fixtures on the gables the doors and the roof are red.

8. The Thomas Edison home in Fort Myers is simple, yet elegant.

Name _____ Date _____

CHAPTER 16　End Marks and Commas　*(pages 142–153)*

Using Commas Before a Noun

◆ Look at the underlined words in each sentence, and add commas where needed. If no commas are needed, make no changes.

1. The classic movie *Field of Dreams* is based on a <u>short readable novel</u> by W. P. Kinsella.

2. *Shoeless Joe* is told by a <u>young idealistic dreamer</u>.

3. A <u>deep mysterious</u> voice tells him to build a baseball field.

4. "Build it and they will come" is the <u>vague and abstract instruction</u>.

5. Ray plows under his <u>fertile Iowa farmland</u>.

6. In the novel the field first includes only a <u>shabby left field</u>.

7. One day the ghost of a <u>gifted handsome outfielder</u> appears.

8. Shoeless Joe Jackson had played for the <u>disgraced baseball team</u>, the 1919 Chicago White Sox.

9. Several players had taken <u>large illegal bribes</u> to lose the World Series.

10. Regardless of the charges, Shoeless Joe had been a <u>great hero</u> of Ray's dead father.

CHAPTER 16   **End Marks and Commas**   *(pages 142–153)*

Using Commas with Adjectives

◆ Add commas where needed in the following sentences. If no commas are needed, make no changes.

1. The United States is generally thought to contain the Northeast Mid-Atlantic Midwest Southwest Southeast and Western regions.

2. The state of Florida is part of the hot sunny Southeast region.

3. The state has a low flat elevation.

4. Lake Okeechobee is one of the largest lakes in the United States and is filled with shallow fresh water.

5. Florida's delightful winter weather attracts many tourists.

6. I looked around the small crowded room for an exit.

7. The difficult lengthy exam tested all our knowledge about the Civil War.

8. The surgeon's knot is useful in tying large, bulky packages.

CHAPTER 16   End Marks and Commas   *(pages 142–153)*

Writing Sentences with Adjectives

◆ Write five sentences, following the instructions below. Use at least two adjectives before the noun in each sentence.

◆ Describe the geography of your region.

1. _____

_____

◆ Describe the geography of your state.

2. _____

_____

◆ Describe the natural resources found in your area.

3. _____

_____

◆ Describe the crops grown in your area.

4. _____

_____

◆ Describe the climate of your area.

5. _____

_____

Name _____ Date _____

Mixed Practice: Commas

◆ Add commas where needed in the following paragraph.

Andrew Wyeth, an American painter, is part of a famous family of artists. Wyeth drew sketched and painted at a very young age. He was encouraged by his father his sisters and family friends. The long difficult study of art began with his famous father at home. Andrew painted people places and experiences familiar to him. His work includes pictures of Pennsylvania and Maine. The pictures show the faces of his neighbors their houses and their land. The paintings generally are not portraits of the people but show them in their everyday ordinary surroundings.

Name _____ Date _____

CHAPTER 16   End Marks and Commas   *(pages 142–153)*

Using Commas with Compound Sentences

◆ Write *I* in the blank if a sentence needs a comma. Write *C* if a sentence is correct.

_____ 1. King Midas loved gold very much and a god granted him the "golden touch."

_____ 2. Midas touched his throne and turned it into gold.

_____ 3. He was very happy with his new power and soon almost everything in his palace became gold.

_____ 4. One day the king called for his dinner and a fine meal was set before him.

_____ 5. He picked up a goblet and raised it to his lips.

_____ 6. His drink instantly hardened to gold and he could not drink it.

_____ 7. Then Midas quickly crammed a piece of bread into his mouth but it turned into a lump of hot gold.

_____ 8. Sometime later he walked through his garden and forgot about his power.

_____ 9. The beautiful roses made the air sweet and Midas loved them.

_____ 10. He gently touched one red rose and it instantly turned to gold.

_____ 11. Just then the king's daughter entered the garden and Midas drew back in horror.

_____ 12. The little girl put her hand on his arm and was turned into a golden statue!

_____ 13. Midas prayed very hard and finally the god heard his pleas.

_____ 14. The king followed the god's instructions and soon the golden touch was gone.

_____ 15. Midas happily threw his arms around his precious daughter and thanked the god for bringing her back to life.

CHAPTER 16   **End Marks and Commas**   *(pages 142–153)*

Correcting for Commas in Compound Sentences

◆ Choose five of the incorrect sentences from the preceding exercise to rewrite, adding commas where needed.

1. _____

   _____

2. _____

   _____

3. _____

   _____

4. _____

   _____

5. _____

   _____

CHAPTER 16 **End Marks and Commas** *(pages 142–153)*

Using Commas with Compound Sentences

◆ Write one compound sentence about each of the following topics. Make sure the clauses in each sentence are related and punctuated correctly.

◆ a fantasy

1. _____

_____

◆ three wishes

2. _____

_____

◆ a hero

3. _____

_____

◆ an important ideal

4. _____

_____

◆ a fear or fears

5. _____

_____

CHAPTER 16 End Marks and Commas *(pages 142–153)*

Using Commas with Introductory Elements

◆ Write *I* in the blank if a sentence needs a comma. Write *C* if a sentence is correct.

_____ 1. To the Europeans' surprise many Native American tribes rose, flourished, and disappeared before the settlers came.

_____ 2. Adapting to the hot desert the Hohokam came to Arizona.

_____ 3. From A.D. 300 to A.D. 1200 they flourished between the Gila River and Salt River valleys.

_____ 4. Their way of life depended heavily on irrigation channels.

_____ 5. In addition to miles of irrigation channels the Hohokam left behind stone pottery and shells.

_____ 6. Historians believe the shells were received from coastal tribes.

_____ 7. Oh the etchings on the shells were done with a kind of acid.

_____ 8. In the area of Utah, Colorado, Arizona, and New Mexico, the Anasazi tribe lived during the same time as the Hohokam.

_____ 9. According to the Spanish conquerors they lived in great stone pueblos because of the heat.

_____ 10. Because drought threatened their large cities the Anasazi broke into small communities.

CHAPTER 16 **End Marks and Commas** *(pages 142–153)*

Correcting for Commas with Introductory Elements

◆ Choose five of the incorrect sentences from the preceding exercise to rewrite, adding commas where needed.

1. _____

_____

2. _____

_____

3. _____

_____

4. _____

_____

5. _____

_____

CHAPTER 16 **End Marks and Commas** *(pages 142–153)*

Using Commas with Introductory Elements

◆ Write five sentences, using each of the following introductory words or phrases. Add commas where needed.

◆ After the long summer vacation

1. _____

_____

◆ As August turned into September

2. _____

_____

◆ Well

3. _____

_____

◆ Fearing the worst from the new situation

4. _____

_____

◆ By the first day

5. _____

_____

CHAPTER 16   End Marks and Commas   *(pages 142–153)*

Using Commas in Dates and Addresses

◆ Write *a* or *b* to indicate the item that is correctly written in each of the following pairs.

_____   1.   a.   Sunday, May 14 2000
         b.   Sunday, May 14, 2000

_____   2.   a.   Dear Maury
         b.   Dear Maury,

_____   3.   a.   Mary New, 129 Jones Street, Los Angeles, CA 90068
         b.   Mary New, 129 Jones Street, Los Angeles, CA, 90068

_____   4.   a.   Thursday August 10, 2000
         b.   Thursday, August 10, 2000

_____   5.   a.   Sincerely
         b.   Sincerely,

_____   6.   a.   Dear John,
         b.   Dear John

_____   7.   a.   Thursday, July 9 1946
         b.   Thursday, July 9, 1946

_____   8.   a.   Dr. John Jahr, Box 456 Farmington, NM 87401
         b.   Dr. John Jahr, Box 456, Farmington, NM 87401

_____   9.   a.   Corpus Christi Texas
         b.   Corpus Christi, Texas

_____   10.   a.   Very truly yours,
          b.   Very truly yours

CHAPTER 16 **End Marks and Commas** *(pages 142–153)*

Using Commas

◆ Follow the directions to write sentences. Be sure to use commas correctly.

◆ Write a sentence that includes the city and state in which you live.

1. _____

_____

◆ Write a sentence that includes the month and year that you were born.

2. _____

_____

◆ Write a sentence that includes the address of your school.

3. _____

_____

◆ Write a sentence that includes the city, state, and ZIP code of someone you know.

4. _____

_____

CHAPTER 16 End Marks and Commas (pages 142–153)

Adding Commas to Sentences

◆ Rewrite each sentence, using commas correctly.

1. The United States capital city was Philadelphia Pennsylvania before the capital was moved to Washington D.C.

_____

_____

2. The White House is located at 1600 Pennsylvania Avenue Washington D.C. 20003.

_____

_____

3. John Adams and his wife hosted the first reception at the White House on January 1 1801.

_____

_____

4. In 1864 Abraham Lincoln sat for Vinnie Ream so that the talented 16-year-old girl could sculpt his image.

_____

_____

5. On July 27 1866 Ream was the first woman to receive a commission for sculpture from the United States Congress.

_____

_____

CHAPTER 16 **End Marks and Commas** *(pages 142–153)*

Using Commas with Direct Address

◆ Write *I* in the blank if commas are used incorrectly in or are missing from the following sentences. Write *C* if a sentence is correct.

_____ 1. Quick, Coach the pitcher needs your help!

_____ 2. Christine don't you bat after, Siela?

_____ 3. On your way to first base Carla, be sure to turn toward second.

_____ 4. Do you like to steal bases, Anna?

_____ 5. Look over at the third-base coach, Keisha, for the signs.

_____ 6. Josie there is only one out in the inning.

_____ 7. Yes, Karen we need to score some runs.

_____ 8. Where is your batter's helmet, Elaine?

_____ 9. Cora you bat, for Betty.

_____ 10. You're our last chance Nancy.

CHAPTER 16 **End Marks and Commas** *(pages 142–153)*

Correcting for Commas with Direct Address

◆ Write the incorrect sentences from the preceding exercise, adding or deleting commas where needed.

1. _____

_____

2. _____

_____

3. _____

_____

4. _____

_____

5. _____

_____

6. _____

_____

7. _____

_____

CHAPTER 16 End Marks and Commas *(pages 142–153)*

Using Commas with Parenthetical Expressions

◆ Write *I* in the blank if commas are used incorrectly in or are missing from a sentence. Write *C* if a sentence is correct.

_____ 1. By the way poetry offers an interesting challenge.

_____ 2. Poetry generally, speaking, is the oldest form of literature.

_____ 3. Poems, I believe, were sung or repeated around the first campfires.

_____ 4. At any rate poems require careful attention.

_____ 5. The most important part of a poem in my opinion, is the meaning of each word.

_____ 6. For example many kinds, of words, can be used.

_____ 7. The words, after all, create feelings and meaning.

_____ 8. Of course poems, also, depend on sound.

_____ 9. I, however like rhyming poems.

_____ 10. Nevertheless, many famous poems do not rhyme.

CHAPTER 16 End Marks and Commas *(pages 142–153)*

Correcting for Commas in Parenthetical Expressions

◆ Write the incorrect sentences from the preceding exercise, adding or deleting commas where needed.

1. _____

_____

2. _____

_____

3. _____

_____

4. _____

_____

5. _____

_____

6. _____

_____

7. _____

_____

CHAPTER 16 End Marks and Commas (pages 142–153)

Writing Sentences with Parenthetical Expressions

◆ Write five sentences, using the following parenthetical expressions as directed. Add commas where needed.

◆ *I hope* in the middle of a sentence

1. _____

_____

◆ *in fact* at the beginning of a sentence

2. _____

_____

◆ *to tell the truth* at the end of a sentence

3. _____

_____

◆ *however* at the beginning of a sentence

4. _____

_____

◆ *for example* in the middle of a sentence

5. _____

_____

CHAPTER 16   End Marks and Commas   *(pages 142–153)*

Using Commas with Appositives

◆ Write *I* in the blank if commas are used incorrectly in or are missing from a sentence. Write *C* if a sentence is correct.

_____   1. Over the years the legend of Paul Bunyan, the most famous lumberjack of all, grew and grew.

_____   2. Paul Bunyan a huge man towered above the trees.

_____   3. His voice once caused a landslide near Pikes Peak a mountain, in Colorado.

_____   4. His mighty blue ox Babe straightened the course of the Whistling River.

_____   5. Hot Biscuit Slim, the cook, was an important member of his logging crew.

_____   6. Cream puffs, the favorite dessert of the crew were baked by the camp cook.

_____   7. Big Swede one of Paul's workers, was known for his accidents.

_____   8. Johnny Inkslinger, the first bookkeeper in the legend, did all the figuring for Paul.

_____   9. It took a bucket brigade of thirty men to fill Johnny's pen a giant rubber hose.

_____   10. The Paul Bunyan legends stories about life in the forest are a big part of American folklore.

CHAPTER 16 **End Marks and Commas** *(pages 142–153)*

Correcting for Commas with Appositives

◆ Write the incorrect sentences from the preceding exercise, adding or deleting commas where needed.

1. _____

_____

2. _____

_____

3. _____

_____

4. _____

_____

5. _____

_____

6. _____

_____

7. _____

_____

CHAPTER 16 End Marks and Commas   *(pages 142–153)*

....

Mixed Practice: Commas

◆ Add commas where needed in the following sentences. If no commas are needed, make no changes.

1. Ellen does your school have a writers' workshop?

2. A writers' workshop a group of five to seven students meets regularly.

3. In fact they discuss their own writing.

4. Most workshops generally speaking focus on one type of writing.

5. This for example might be fiction or poetry or plays.

6. However some workshops can be unusual.

7. One workshop The Fourteen Liners concentrates just on sonnets.

8. That is correct Ellen.

9. Other workshops may focus on science fiction, horror, or mysteries.

10. Joyce Carol Oates a famous modern writer wrote a book about writers' workshops.

CHAPTER 16 End Marks and Commas *(pages 142–153)*

Using Commas with Nonessential Elements

◆ Write *C* in the blank if a sentence is correctly punctuated. Write *I* if a sentence is incorrectly punctuated.

_____ 1. People who help other people are heroes.

_____ 2. Volunteer work which happens all over the world is good citizenship.

_____ 3. In fact, there is a computer database that lists willing volunteers in a community.

_____ 4. This computer program, which is easily downloaded, also keeps track of the people, being served.

_____ 5. It also does accounting which is important for state funding.

_____ 6. However, the most important work is done by people who give of their time.

_____ 7. Often volunteers work in shelters that feed homeless people.

_____ 8. These volunteers who come from all walks of life serve food.

_____ 9. Some heroes visit hospital patients who have no families.

_____ 10. These "candy stripers" who wear uniforms with stripes help the nurses.

CHAPTER 16   End Marks and Commas   *(pages 142–153)*

Correcting for Commas with Appositives

◆ Write the incorrect sentences from the preceding exercise, adding or deleting commas where needed.

1. _____

_____

2. _____

_____

3. _____

_____

4. _____

_____

5. _____

_____

CHAPTER 16 **End Marks and Commas** *(pages 142–153)*

Writing Sentences

◆ Write five sentences, following the instructions below. Use commas where needed for nonessential phrases and clauses.

◆ Write a sentence identifying your hero, and use a clause to describe him or her.

1. _____

_____

◆ Write a sentence that tells where your hero serves, and use a phrase to describe the place.

2. _____

_____

◆ Write a sentence that describes the people or the cause the hero helps, and use a clause to describe the people or the cause.

3. _____

_____

◆ Write a sentence that tells about your hero, and then use a phrase to tell about the hero.

4. _____

_____

◆ Write a sentence that describes the effect of your hero's work, and use a clause to offer specific details about that effect.

5. _____

_____

CHAPTER 16   **End Marks and Commas**   *(pages 142–153)*

Mixed Practice: Commas

◆ Add commas where needed in the following sentences. If the sentence is correct, make no changes.

1. Pee Wee Reese the Brooklyn Dodger shortstop was inducted into the Baseball Hall of Fame in 1984.

2. Reese who helped Jackie Robinson adjust to major league baseball was born in Kentucky.

3. Roger Kahn's book *The Boys of Summer* tells how Reese helped baseball integration.

4. Reese however was also a great baseball player.

5. The well-liked man was an eight-time All-Star hitting 126 home runs with 885 RBIs.

6. Reese the heart and soul of the Dodgers stole thirty bases in 1930.

7. In 1947, Reese who battled cancer late in life led his league in runs scored.

8. Reese a man of many nicknames was also called "The Little Colonel."

CHAPTER 17 Italics and Quotation Marks *(pages 154–161)*

Using Italics (Underlining)

◆ Write *a* or *b* to indicate the item that is correctly underlined in each of the following pairs. For the names of newspapers, magazines, and vehicles, remember that the word *the* is not part of the title.

_____ 1. a. the nonfiction <u>book</u> Profiles in <u>Courage</u> by John F. Kennedy

b. the nonfiction book <u>Profiles in Courage</u> by John F. Kennedy

_____ 2. a. a steamboat called the <u>Clermont</u>

b. a steamboat called <u>the Clermont</u>

_____ 3. a. the letters <u>g and q</u>

b. the letters <u>g</u> and <u>q</u>

_____ 4. a. the newspaper <u>the Nashville Banner</u>

b. the newspaper the <u>Nashville Banner</u>

_____ 5. a. the movie <u>The Iron Giant</u>

b. the movie The <u>Iron Giant</u>

_____ 6. a. the Broadway play <u>Cats</u>

b. the <u>Broadway play Cats</u>

_____ 7. a. the famous painting The <u>Starry Night</u>

b. the famous painting <u>The Starry Night</u>

_____ 8. a. the space shuttle <u>Discovery</u>

b. the <u>space shuttle Discovery</u>

_____ 9. a. the movie <u>Flubber</u> with Robin Williams

b. the movie <u>Flubber with Robin Williams</u>

_____ 10. a. the magazine American <u>Girl</u>

b. the magazine <u>American Girl</u>

CHAPTER 17   Italics and Quotation Marks   *(pages 154–161)*

Using Underlining Correctly

◆ <u>Underline</u> where needed in the following sentences.

1. The Los Angeles Times is a big newspaper.

2. Readers can read a review of a book such as Richard Peck's A Long Way from Chicago.

3. The reviews are longer than those in Newsweek.

4. The letter i comes before e in the word review.

5. A newspaper will announce the showing of paintings such as Van Gogh's Sunflowers.

6. The theater page will review a play such as Beauty and the Beast.

7. A feature article might give the history of the space station Mir.

8. Every newspaper in the country reviewed the movie Star Wars: Episode One.

9. Music critics review operas such as Carmen.

10. Write your 7s so that they do not look like 9s.

Name _____ Date _____

CHAPTER 17   Italics and Quotation Marks   *(pages 154–161)*

Punctuating Titles Correctly

◆ Read the following sentences. Write *C* in the blank if the quotation marks and underlining in a sentence are used correctly. Write *I* if the quotation marks and underlining are used incorrectly.

_____ 1. The song <u>Guinevere</u> is from the musical "Camelot".

_____ 2. I read the poem "Paul Revere's Ride" in speech class.

_____ 3. <u>The Buck in the Hills</u> is a short story about hunting.

_____ 4. We are studying the chapter "The Colonies Win Freedom" in our history book, <u>The Heritage of America</u>.

_____ 5. The article <u>A Lost Son Is Found</u> was published in Newsweek.

_____ 6. "The Ugly Duckling" is a one-act play.

_____ 7. I copied Helen Hunt Jackson's short poem "September."

_____ 8. Julie loves the song Tomorrow from the musical <u>Annie</u>.

_____ 9. <u>Sponges</u> is the name of a chapter in our textbook Life Science.

_____ 10. We read the article "India Today" in this week's Time.

Copyright © Perfection Learning® All rights reserved.

326   Many Voices Language • Level G • Chapter 17: Italics and Quotation Marks

CHAPTER 17   Italics and Quotation Marks   *(pages 154–161)*

Correcting for Punctuation of Titles

◆ Rewrite the incorrect sentences from the preceding exercise, using underlining and quotation marks correctly.

1. _____

_____

2. _____

_____

3. _____

_____

4. _____

_____

5. _____

_____

6. _____

_____

Name _____ Date _____

Writing Sentences with Titles

◆ Write five sentences that answer the following questions.

◆ What is the title of your literature textbook?

1. _____

   _____

◆ What is your favorite short story in that book?

2. _____

   _____

◆ What is your favorite poem?

3. _____

   _____

◆ What is the title of your science textbook?

4. _____

   _____

◆ What chapter in your science textbook are you studying now?

5. _____

   _____

CHAPTER 17 Italics and Quotation Marks *(pages 154–161)*

Using Quotation Marks with Direct Quotations

◆ Read the following sentences. Write *C* in the blank if a sentence is punctuated correctly. Write *I* if a sentence is punctuated incorrectly.

_____ 1. "I once had a temperature of 103°F, said Devon."

_____ 2. The nurse said that a temperature that high was a sign of infection.

_____ 3. "Sometimes, she added," "a lukewarm bath can bring down a temperature."

_____ 4. Kayla said, "My mom gives me medicine when I have a fever."

_____ 5. "If a fever lasts more than a few days, the nurse continued, you should probably see a doctor.

_____ 6. "The doctor may be able to tell what kind of infection you have," she explained.

_____ 7. She said "that the infection could be caused by bacteria."

_____ 8. In that case, "she went on," you might need to take antibiotics.

_____ 9. "Don't ask for antibiotics if you don't need them," the nurse urged.

_____ 10. "If you do, she explained, your body might eventually develop germs that are stronger than the antibiotics."

Name _____ Date _____

Punctuating Quotations Correctly

◆ Rewrite the incorrectly punctuated sentences in the preceding exercise, using quotation marks correctly. Be sure to place periods and commas inside the ending quotation marks.

1. _____

   _____

2. _____

   _____

3. _____

   _____

4. _____

   _____

5. _____

   _____

6. _____

   _____

CHAPTER 17 Italics and Quotation Marks *(pages 154–161)*

Using Capital Letters with Direct Quotations

◆ Write *C* in the blank if capital letters are used correctly in a sentence. Write *I* if capital letters are used incorrectly in a sentence.

_____ 1. The Boy Scout leader said, "we are here to discuss how to help our community."

_____ 2. He continued, "Our community has many different needs."

_____ 3. "We can identify these needs," he went on, "by listing the groups who have asked for our help."

_____ 4. "first, there are those who need food and shelter," he said.

_____ 5. "Among the other groups," he added, "Are the young, the elderly, and the disabled."

_____ 6. "It is important," he said, "to think of this help as community service and not as charity."

_____ 7. "Volunteers make our whole community stronger," He claimed.

_____ 8. "By helping others," he insisted, "You also help yourself."

_____ 9. "It is your community," he said. "It is your responsibility."

_____ 10. The Boy Scout leader concluded, "come join your community."

CHAPTER 17 Italics and Quotation Marks *(pages 154–161)*

Capitalizing Direct Quotations Correctly

◆ Rewrite the incorrect sentences from the preceding exercise, using capital letters correctly.

1. _____

_____

2. _____

_____

3. _____

_____

4. _____

_____

5. _____

_____

6. _____

_____

CHAPTER 17 Italics and Quotation Marks *(pages 154–161)*

Using Commas with Direct Quotations

◆ Write *C* in the blank if commas are used correctly in a sentence. Write *I* if commas are used incorrectly.

_____ 1. "Chuckwallas are playful lizards", Ms. Poe said.

_____ 2. "They live in the desert," she added.

_____ 3. She continued ",Chuckwallas play hide-and-seek."

_____ 4. "They run to a hiding place," she explained "and then peep out to spy on the others."

_____ 5. Ms. Poe went on, "Sometimes a chuckwalla will jump out and grab another's tail just for fun."

_____ 6. "Snakes and birds" Ms. Poe added, "sometimes attack them.

_____ 7. She added, "A chuckwalla can easily protect itself."

_____ 8. "It crawls in between rocks", she explained "and blows up like a balloon."

_____ 9. She added "An enemy cannot pull it loose."

_____ 10. "When the attacker gives up," she concluded, "the chuckwalla lets out the air and scurries off."

CHAPTER 17   Italics and Quotation Marks   *(pages 154–161)*

Correcting for Commas in Direct Quotations

◆ Rewrite the incorrect sentences from the preceding exercise, using commas correctly.

1. _____

   _____

2. _____

   _____

3. _____

   _____

4. _____

   _____

5. _____

   _____

6. _____

   _____

CHAPTER 17 Italics and Quotation Marks *(pages 154–161)*

Using End Marks with Direct Quotations

◆ Write *C* in the blank if the end marks in a sentence are used correctly. Write *I* if end marks are used incorrectly.

_____ 1. "Have you ever hunted for pearls" asked Linda?

_____ 2. "No," Mr. Quinn answered, "but I would like to find one sometime!"

_____ 3. "Is diving for pearls dangerous?" Hector asked.

_____ 4. "It can be extremely dangerous!" Mr. Quinn exclaimed.

_____ 5. Taylor asked, "Do pearl divers know which oysters contain pearls?"

_____ 6. "They can't tell," Mr. Quinn replied, "until they look inside the shell."

_____ 7. "What happens to the oyster once the pearl is removed?" she asked.

_____ 8. Mr. Quinn explained, "A diver returns the oyster to the water?"

_____ 9. "The diver hopes," Mr. Quinn continued, "that the same oyster will make another pearl."

_____ 10. "What a job," Linda exclaimed, "No wonder pearls are so expensive!"

CHAPTER 17 **Italics and Quotation Marks**   *(pages 154–161)*

Correcting for End Marks in Direct Quotations

◆ Rewrite the incorrectly punctuated quotations from the preceding exercise, using end marks correctly.

1. _____

   _____

2. _____

   _____

3. _____

   _____

4. _____

   _____

CHAPTER 17 Italics and Quotation Marks *(pages 154–161)*

Mixed Practice: Direct Quotations

◆ Add quotation marks, commas, end marks, and capital letters where needed in the sentences below.

1. many people do not realize that the crow is a very smart bird Mr. Adams said

2. he added a crow can outwit hawks and most people

3. does putting a scarecrow in a cornfield really help Andrea asked

4. that is a big mistake exclaimed Mr. Adams.

5. many crows he explained use the scarecrows as lookout posts

6. one crow he continued will act as a guard for a flock of crows in a cornfield

7. Sam asked what does the crow do if it senses danger

8. it caws a danger signal to the others Mr. Adams said and they all fly away

9. a team of three crows will also work together to get food from an animal Mr. Adams added

10. how do they do that Beth asked

11. a crow lands on each side of the animal Mr. Adams answered and pretends to steal the animal's food.

12. then the third crow he continued swoops down and snatches the food

13. that's amazing Jeff exclaimed

14. these smart birds also like to have plenty of fun Mr. Adams said

CHAPTER 17 Italics and Quotation Marks *(pages 154–161)*

Using Dialogue

◆ Read aloud the following dialogue between Gina and Connie. Put a paragraph symbol (¶) in each place where a new paragraph should begin.

Gina exclaimed, "What a good idea! I should do that too." "I hope she has some good ideas for me," Connie responded. "I'm not sure what kind of work I'd like to do." "I'm sure she'll be helpful," Gina said. "Let me know what you find out," she added. "Then I can make an appointment too." "Sure," said Connie. "Maybe we can work together somewhere."

CHAPTER 17 **Italics and Quotation Marks** *(pages 154–161)*

Writing Dialogue Correctly

◆ Rewrite the preceding dialogue correctly, beginning a new paragraph each time the speaker changes.

_____

_____

_____

_____

_____

_____

_____

_____

_____

_____

_____

_____

_____

_____

_____

CHAPTER 17   Italics and Quotation Marks   *(pages 154–161)*

Quoting Long Passages

◆ Imagine that you are quoting the following passage in a report. Add quotation marks where they belong.

1. In other words, how good really is a house built by volunteers?

2. Hurricane Andrew, which destroyed thousands of houses, didn't take down a single Habitat house. That's how good.

3. All twenty-seven houses built by Habitat for Humanity in south Florida were still standing with only the slightest of damage. And some were right in the hurricane's path. On Guava Street in west Perrine, all that was left of the neighborhood were splintered trees, trashed cars, headless palms, and yards full of debris, which once had been houses . . . except for four Habitat houses standing side-by-side in a sea of devastation.

—Millard Fuller, *A Simple, Decent Place to Live*

CHAPTER 17 Italics and Quotation Marks *(pages 154–161)*

Mixed Practice: Punctuation and Italics

◆ Add underlining, quotation marks, commas, and end marks where needed in the following sentences. Remember that only a sentence with a speaker tag should be considered a direct quotation.

1. Theodore H. White was a reporter for Time magazine

2. He is different from the T. H. White who wrote the book The Once and Future King

3. White wrote an article called The American Idea for The New York Times

4. In his article White wrote Americans are a nation born of an idea

5. All men are created equal Thomas Jefferson wrote in 1776

6. Theodore White said Jefferson himself could not have imagined the reach of his call across the world in times to come

7. Why did Jefferson use the word men instead of the word people

8. In 1848 Elizabeth Cady Stanton said All men and women are created equal

9. Along with Susan B. Anthony, Stanton coedited three volumes of a book called History of Woman Suffrage.

10. Anthony published a weekly journal called The Revolution

11. Charlotte Perkins Gilman also argued for women's rights in her magazine called the Forerunner.

12. The word suffragette was used to describe a woman who fought for the right to vote.

CHAPTER 18 Other Punctuation   *(pages 162–173)*

Forming Possessive Singular Nouns

◆ Rewrite each of the following phrases, using the possessive form.

1. the fields of the farmer _____

2. the tires of the bus _____

3. the whiskers of the cat _____

4. the skill of the typist _____

5. the role of the actor _____

6. muffins belonging to Sue _____

7. end of the day _____

8. job of my mother _____

9. the lid of the box _____

10. the rays of the sun _____

CHAPTER 18 **Other Punctuation**   *(pages 162–173)*

Using Apostrophes with Singular Possessive Nouns

◆ Write five sentences, using five of the possessive phrases you formed in the preceding exercise.

1. _____

_____

2. _____

_____

3. _____

_____

4. _____

_____

5. _____

_____

CHAPTER 18   **Other Punctuation**   *(pages 162–173)*

Forming Possessive Plural Nouns

◆ Rewrite each of the following phrases, using the possessive form.

1. playground of the children _____

2. feathers of the turkeys _____

3. lids of the boxes _____

4. mealtimes of the puppies _____

5. howls of the wolves _____

6. nest of the birds _____

7. migration of the geese _____

8. sizes of the shoes _____

9. suits of the women _____

10. claws of the tigers _____

CHAPTER 18 Other Punctuation *(pages 162–173)*

Forming Possessive Nouns

◆ Rewrite each of the following phrases, using the correct possessive form. Notice that some nouns are singular and some are plural.

1. the ringing of the alarm clock _____

2. the rising of the sun _____

3. the aroma of the coffee _____

4. the crackling of cereal _____

5. the sounds of appliances _____

6. the yawns of slow risers _____

7. the arrival of the newspaper _____

8. the schedules of the buses _____

9. the conversations of the children _____

10. the laughter of the women _____

11. the music of the radio _____

12. the riding class of the girls _____

13. the homework of Mercedes _____

14. the food selection of the pantry _____

CHAPTER 18 **Other Punctuation** *(pages 162–173)*

Writing Sentences: Using Possessive Nouns

◆ Write five sentences, using five of the possessive phrases you formed in the preceding exercise.

1. _____

_____

2. _____

_____

3. _____

_____

4. _____

_____

5. _____

_____

CHAPTER 18   **Other Punctuation**   *(pages 162–173)*

Replacing Phrases with Possessive Nouns

◆ Rewrite each sentence, replacing the underlined phrases with possessive nouns.

1. The desks of the students await their arrival.

   _____

   _____

2. The heat of the building is turned on.

   _____

   _____

3. The hands of the clock inch toward eight o'clock.

   _____

   _____

4. The coats of the girls are hung up.

   _____

   _____

5. The briefcases of the teachers are opened.

   _____

   _____

6. The music of the band floats across the room.

   _____

   _____

CHAPTER 18   Other Punctuation   *(pages 162–173)*

Using Possessive Pronouns

◆ Write *C* in the blank if the correct possessive form is used in a sentence. Write *I* if the incorrect form is used.

_____ 1. Everyone's report must include library research.

_____ 2. Is your's about computers?

_____ 3. Jason and I worked on our's together.

_____ 4. Its title is "Medical Miracles."

_____ 5. Does your report list all of your sources?

_____ 6. Is this library book hers'?

_____ 7. Is anyones report finished yet?

_____ 8. Hector finished his's on Monday.

_____ 9. Kayla and Erin have finished theirs, too.

_____ 10. I hope no one's grade depends on this one assignment.

CHAPTER 18   Other Punctuation   *(pages 162–173)*

Correcting for Possessive Pronouns

◆ Rewrite the incorrect sentences from the previous exercise, using the correct forms of possessive pronouns.

1. _____

_____

2. _____

_____

3. _____

_____

4. _____

_____

5. _____

_____

CHAPTER 18 **Other Punctuation** *(pages 162–173)*

Writing Sentences

◆ Write five sentences using possessive pronouns. Follow the directions given below.

◆ Write a sentence about the bike belonging to him.

1. _____

   _____

◆ Write a sentence about the house belonging to them.

2. _____

   _____

◆ Write a question asking if a pen belongs to anyone.

3. _____

   _____

◆ Write a sentence about the price of it.

4. _____

   _____

◆ Write a sentence about the favorite song of everyone.

5. _____

   _____

CHAPTER 18 Other Punctuation   (pages 162–173)

....

Mixed Practice: Possessive Nouns and Pronouns

◆ Write the correct form of any incorrect possessive nouns and pronouns in the following sentences. If a sentence is correct, make no changes.

1. Eleanor Roosevelt was President Franklin Roosevelts' wife.

   _____

2. She took her job as the nation's First Lady very seriously.

   _____

3. Mrs. Roosevelt visited battlefields and raised many soldiers spirits.

   _____

4. She visited coal miners and tried to improve they're lives.

   _____

5. Mrs. Roosevelt spoke up for womens' rights.

   _____

6. She also supported African Americans' rights.

   _____

7. Many ideas that the President suggested were actually her's.

   _____

8. She believed that doing useful work was everyone's responsibility.

   _____

9. After World War II, she helped the United Nations with its work on human rights.

   _____

CHAPTER 18 Other Punctuation *(pages 162–173)*

Forming Contractions

◆ Write the contraction for each pair of words.

1. there is _____

2. would not _____

3. they are _____

4. will not _____

5. we have _____

6. were not _____

7. had not _____

8. who is _____

9. do not _____

10. are not _____

11. let us _____

12. you are _____

13. I have _____

14. I am _____

15. I will _____

CHAPTER 18 **Other Punctuation** *(pages 162–173)*

Contraction or Possessive Pronoun?

◆ <u>Underline</u> the correct word in parentheses.

1. (There's, Theirs) a snake!

2. Did (your, you're) science class ever study snakes?

3. That snake was once rattling (it's, its) tail.

4. (Who's, Whose) going to touch it?

5. I think (you're, your) interested in snakes.

6. (It's, Its) going to be an interesting class.

7. Did you see (they're, their) lab manual?

8. I don't know (who's, whose) rubber gloves these are.

9. (There's, Theirs) are on the table.

10. (They're, Their) starting (they're, their) experiment.

CHAPTER 18   **Other Punctuation**   *(pages 162–173)*

Writing Sentences with Contractions

◆ Make contractions from the following words. Then write sentences using the contractions.

1. it is_____

_____

_____

2. there is_____

_____

_____

3. they are_____

_____

_____

4. you are_____

_____

_____

5. who is_____

_____

_____

6. we have_____

_____

_____

CHAPTER 18 **Other Punctuation** *(pages 162–173)*

Using Contractions and Possessive Pronouns

◆ Rewrite the incorrect sentences, using the correct contraction or possessive pronoun. If a sentence is correct, make no changes.

1. Whose picking you up after school today?

_____

_____

2. I hope your ready because your bus is here.

_____

_____

3. It's too late for them to check their lockers now.

_____

_____

4. Who's notebook is this?

_____

_____

5. There's a backpack on that desk.

_____

_____

6. It's zipper is broken.

_____

_____

CHAPTER 18　**Other Punctuation**　*(pages 162–173)*

Using Apostrophes

◆ Write the plural form of each of the following letters, symbols, or words used as words.

1. a _____

2. c _____

3. B _____

4. I _____

5. + _____

6. # _____

7. 2 _____

8. 1960 _____

9. and _____

10. hi _____

CHAPTER 18 Other Punctuation (pages 162–173)

Writing Sentences Using Plurals

◆ Write five sentences using five of the plurals you formed in the preceding exercise.

1. _____

_____

2. _____

_____

3. _____

_____

4. _____

_____

5. _____

_____

CHAPTER 18 Other Punctuation   *(pages 162–173)*

Mixed Practice: Apostrophes

◆ Add an apostrophe where needed to the underlined words. If no apostrophe is needed, make no changes.

1. By the <u>1700s</u>, both France and Great Britain were powerful nations.

2. In North America, both nations wanted to make the colonies <u>theirs</u>.

3. Each side sought the <u>Native Americans</u> help.

4. <u>Frances</u> goal was to build trade in North America.

5. <u>Great Britains</u> objective was different.

6. It wanted to add territory to <u>its</u> empire.

7. The *is* were dotted in each treaty with the Native Americans.

8. <u>Everyones</u> life was changed in the colonies because of both European <u>nations</u> greed.

9. The <u>mens</u> lives were changed because they became soldiers.

10. <u>Womens</u> and <u>childrens</u> lives were changed because they didn't know whether their husbands and fathers were coming home.

CHAPTER 18 Other Punctuation *(pages 162–173)*

Using Commas and Semicolons with Compound Sentences

◆ Write *C* in the blank if a sentence is punctuated correctly. Write *I* if a sentence is punctuated incorrectly.

_____ 1. Mesa Verde is located in southwestern Colorado, it is near the city of Cortez.

_____ 2. The Anasazi people built the cliff houses; some of the buildings are four stories high.

_____ 3. The Anasazi people lived at Mesa Verde for almost one hundred years, then the people disappeared from the area.

_____ 4. Centuries later the Ute Indians moved into the area, but they stayed away from the deserted cliff houses.

_____ 5. Spanish settlers also explored the area; but they never saw the abandoned buildings.

_____ 6. Two ranchers discovered the buildings in 1888 and in the 1890s, curious visitors flocked to the ancient settlement.

_____ 7. Many visitors stole precious souvenirs from the area, then an angry newspaper reporter complained.

_____ 8. In 1906, Congress decided to protect the ancient dwellings; it passed legislation that created Mesa Verde National Park.

_____ 9. The Cliff Palace is the park's most popular attraction, and we decided to take a tour of it.

_____ 10. Visitors to the Balcony House must climb a thirty-two-foot ladder to get inside, I decided to try it.

CHAPTER 18 **Other Punctuation** *(pages 162–173)*

Punctuating Compound Sentences Correctly

◆ Rewrite the incorrectly punctuated sentences from the preceding exercise, using commas and semicolons correctly.

1. _____

_____

2. _____

_____

3. _____

_____

4. _____

_____

5. _____

_____

6. _____

_____

CHAPTER 18   Other Punctuation   *(pages 162–173)*

Writing Sentences Using Commas and Semicolons

◆ Write sentences that follow the directions. Use commas and semicolons correctly in your sentences.

◆ Write a compound sentence joined by the conjunction *and*.

1. _____

_____

◆ Rewrite correctly the same compound sentence you just wrote, taking out the conjunction *and*.

2. _____

_____

◆ Write a compound sentence joined by the conjunction *but*.

3. _____

_____

◆ Rewrite correctly the same compound sentence you just wrote, taking out the conjunction *but*.

4. _____

_____

CHAPTER 18 **Other Punctuation** *(pages 162–173)*

Using Semicolons

◆ Write *C* in the blank if a sentence is punctuated correctly. Write *I* if a sentence is punctuated incorrectly.

_____ 1. Other South American nations include Chile, located on the South Pacific coast, Argentina, reaching down to the continent's tip, and Uruguay, located on the South Atlantic coast.

_____ 2. The three nations' capitals are Santiago, Chile, Buenos Aires, Argentina, and Montevideo, Uruguay.

_____ 3. Chile's population includes people of European, Indian, and other backgrounds; and its primary language is Spanish.

_____ 4. Chile's crops include wheat, corn, and grapes, but its main export is copper.

_____ 5. Argentina's major cities include Buenos Aires, with thirteen million people, Cordoba, with more than a million people, and Moron, with at least half a million people.

_____ 6. Languages spoken in Argentina include Spanish, English, Italian, German, and French; and most of the country's population is of the Roman Catholic faith.

_____ 7. Argentina exports meat, wheat, and corn; and it imports machinery, chemicals, fuel, and other industrial products.

_____ 8. Uruguay's major cities include Montevideo, Salto, and Paysandú, but Montevideo is much larger than any of the other cities.

_____ 9. In order of size, the nations are Argentina, with more than a million square miles, Chile, covering about 290,000 square miles, and Uruguay, having only 68,000 square miles.

_____ 10. In order of population, the nations are Argentina, with thirty-four million people; Chile, with fourteen million people; and Uruguay, with only three million people.

CHAPTER 18 **Other Punctuation** *(pages 162–173)*

Punctuating Sentences with Semicolons

◆ Rewrite the incorrectly punctuated sentences from the preceding exercise,
using semicolons correctly.

1. _____

_____

2. _____

_____

3. _____

_____

4. _____

_____

5. _____

_____

6. _____

_____

7. _____

_____

CHAPTER 18 **Other Punctuation** *(pages 162–173)*

Using Colons

◆ Write *C* in the blank if a sentence or phrase is punctuated correctly. Write *I* if a sentence is punctuated incorrectly.

_____ 1. Some popular vacations include the following luxury cruises, adventure trips, and European travel.

_____ 2. Travel agencies recommend three cruise destinations: Alaska, the Caribbean, and the Mediterranean.

_____ 3. Some popular cruise ships are the *Silver Cloud,* the *Wind Song,* and the *Whisper Spirit.*

_____ 4. The great thing about a cruise is no one has to get up at 6 30 A.M.

_____ 5. Travel brochures offer the following adventures motorcycle trips in Costa Rica, polar bear viewing in Canada, or an island tour of Hawaii.

_____ 6. If you go on an adventure vacation, be sure to take: a camera, sunscreen, insect repellent, and a first-aid kit.

_____ 7. There are three popular vacation cities in Europe Paris, London, and Amsterdam.

_____ 8. Travelers' favorite American cities include New York City, Orlando, and Las Vegas.

_____ 9. A South American vacation could include adventures in: Ecuador, Venezuela, Colombia, or Peru.

_____ 10. Dear Sir

CHAPTER 18 **Other Punctuation** *(pages 162–173)*

Using Colons

◆ Rewrite the incorrectly punctuated sentences from the exercise on the preceding page, adding or removing colons where needed.

1. _____

_____

2. _____

_____

3. _____

_____

4. _____

_____

5. _____

_____

6. _____

_____

7. _____

_____

CHAPTER 18 **Other Punctuation** *(pages 162–173)*

Mixed Practice: Commas, Semicolons, and Colons

◆ Add or remove commas, semicolons, and colons as needed from the following
sentences. If a sentence is correct, make no changes.

1. Meriwether Lewis and William Clark were important explorers, they opened up
   the West for expansion.

2. Their expedition set off from St. Louis, Missouri, in the spring of 1804, and they
   reached the Pacific Ocean in November of 1805.

3. The long trip was a success, and President Jefferson was delighted with their
   discoveries.

4. The two adventurers collected information on the following the people, plants,
   animals, and geography of the West.

5. Their crew included: soldiers, interpreters, and one slave.

6. The list of obstacles was endless: rivers, mountains, weather, and animals.

7. In a village in North Dakota, they met a Shoshone Indian woman named
   Sacajawea, she became their guide.

8. Sacajawea knew the land and the local tribes; and her knowledge saved the
   expedition.

9. Lewis and Clark explored: the Missouri River, the Columbia River, and the Snake
   River.

10. Afterward, they returned to the East and reported on the wonders they had seen;
    their reports inspired settlers to move farther westward.

CHAPTER 18 **Other Punctuation** *(pages 162–173)*

Using Hyphens

◆ Write each word, adding a hyphen or hyphens to show where it can be correctly divided. If a word should not be divided, write *no* after the word.

1. hamster _____

2. among _____

3. galaxy _____

4. make _____

5. about _____

6. liquid _____

7. item _____

8. single _____

9. surprise _____

10. strong _____

11. captain _____

12. build _____

13. action _____

14. opal _____

15. trespass _____

CHAPTER 18 Other Punctuation (pages 162–173)

Correcting Sentences with Hyphens

◆ In the following paragraph, correct the incorrect use of hyphens at the ends of the lines. If a word can be hyphenated, move the hyphen to an appropriate place. If a word cannot be hyphenated, write it as one word. If the word is correctly hyphenated, leave it blank.

Jonas Salk was a scient- _____

ist who studied bacteria at the U- _____

niversity of Pittsburgh. In 1955, he _____

made a discovery that changed the wor- _____

ld. He had made a vaccine that could _____

protect children from a disea- _____

se called polio.

In the early 1900s, polio had cri- _____

ppled or killed nearly a million Americ-_____

ans. Salk's vaccine was soon being give-_____

n to America's children as an injec-_____

tion. It was very effective, but soon an e- _____

ven better polio vaccine was discovered. _____

A scientist named Albert Sabin created a poli- _____

o vaccine that children could take oral- _____

ly. Now children can be protected from polio _____

without even having a shot.

CHAPTER 18 **Other Punctuation** *(pages 162–173)*

Using Hyphens

◆ Write *C* in the blank if a sentence is punctuated correctly. Write *I* if a sentence is punctuated incorrectly.

_____ 1. The student council met in the home econom-

ics room yesterday afternoon.

_____ 2. Twenty two students attended the meeting.

_____ 3. Three fourths of the members answered the roll.

_____ 4. Four-teen members offered suggestions from the student body.

_____ 5. Many suggestions were about improving school lunches by offering more

ham-burgers, hot-dogs, and french-fries.

_____ 6. The secretary wrote minutes in her note-book.

_____ 7. A motion was made to spend thirty-three dollars for decorations for the

homecoming dance.

_____ 8. The motion passed with a three fourths majority.

_____ 9. One-fourth of the council voted against the idea.

_____ 10. At the end of the meeting, the members pose-

d for their yearbook picture.

CHAPTER 18 Other Punctuation   *(pages 162–173)*

Using Hyphens Correctly

◆ Rewrite the incorrectly punctuated sentences from the preceding exercise,
adding or deleting hyphens where needed.

1. _____

_____

2. _____

_____

3. _____

_____

4. _____

_____

5. _____

_____

6. _____

_____

7. _____

_____

CHAPTER 18   Other Punctuation   *(pages 162–173)*

Mixed Practice: Punctuation

◆ Rewrite each sentence, adding apostrophes, semicolons, colons, and hyphens where needed.

1. Todays school lunch includes the following turkey, green beans, mashed potatoes, apple pie, and milk.

   _____

   _____

2. Good nutrition is vital to a teenagers health and well being.

   _____

   _____

3. One third of the student body does not eat the meal offered in our schools lunchroom.

   _____

   _____

4. Everyones appetite is different, but balanced nutrition is important to success in school.

   _____

   _____

5. Some students eat only "junk food" cake, candy, and soda.

   _____

   _____

Notes